Radio Systems II

A textbook covering the Level II syllabus
of the Technician Education Council

D C Green

M Tech, CEng, MIERE
Senior Lecturer in Telecommunication Engineering
Willesden College of Technology

Pitman

PITMAN BOOKS LIMITED
128 Long Acre, London WC2E 9AN

Associated Companies
Pitman Publishing Pty Ltd, Melbourne
Pitman Publishing New Zealand Ltd, Wellington

© D. C. Green 1978

First published in Great Britain 1978
Reprinted 1980, 1981, 1982, 1983

Text set in 10/12 Times Roman.
Printed and bound in Great Britain
at The Pitman Press, Bath

ISBN 0 272 01126 X

Contents

Preface

This book has been written to provide an introduction to the principles of radio engineering and is aimed primarily at the intending radiotechnician. A technician working in the field in radiocommunication must have a good knowledge of radio-frequency transmission lines and aerials since these are essential components of any radio system. He should also understand the various ways in which a radio wave may be propagated from the radio transmitter to the radio receiver. In addition, the technician should be well acquainted with the principles of operation of radio transmitters and receivers and the circuitry employed within them.

The first three chapters of this book introduce the reader to the basic principles of r.f. lines, aerials and radio wave propagation. Next, chapter four discusses the circuits used in radio receivers such as r.f. and a.f. amplifiers, oscillators and detectors. The remaining chapters of the book then cover, in turn, radio receivers, radio transmitters and radiocommunication systems. Thus, the book provides a comprehensive introduction to radiocommunication systems and should prove to be suitable for any introductory course in radio engineering.

The Technician Education Council (TEC) have introduced a scheme for the education of electronic and telecommunication technicians. The scheme consists of a number of units that a technician is expected to be able to complete within a period of three years part-time study. This book provides a complete coverage of the level II unit Radio Systems II. The contents of the unit have been written by the TEC in the form of learning objectives which specify the aims of the units and the means by which a student can demonstrate his attainment of each objective. The learning objectives for Radio Systems II are given at the end of the book and acknowledgement is made to the TEC for their permission to reproduce these objectives. The council reserves the right to amend the contents of its unit at any time.

Many worked examples are provided in the text to illustrate the principles that have been discussed and each chapter concludes with a number of exercises. Many of these exercises have been taken from past City and Guilds examination papers and grateful acknowledgement for permission to do so is made to the Institute. Answers to the numerical problems are to be found at the end of the book; the answers given are the responsibility of the author and are not necessarily endorsed by the Institute.

D.C.G.

The following abbreviations for other titles in this series are used in the text:

TSII: Transmission Systems II
EII: Electronics II
EIII: Electronics III

1 Loss-free Radio-frequency Transmission Lines

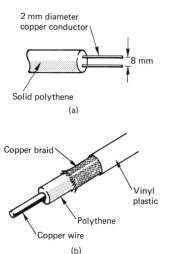

2 mm diameter
copper conductor

8 mm

Solid polythene

(a)

Copper braid

Vinyl plastic

Polythene

Copper wire

(b)

Fig. 1.1 Construction of (a) a twin cable and (b) a coaxial cable

Introduction

A transmission line consists of a pair of conductors that are separated from one another by a dielectric, and are of such a length that the time taken for a voltage or a current applied at one end of the conductors to produce an output at the other end is an appreciable fraction of the periodic time of the voltage or current waveform. Two main types of transmission line are available: the two-wire or twin line shown in Fig. 1.1a; and the coaxial or concentric line shown in Fig. 1.1b.

The basic principles of operation of a transmission line and the constructional details of different types of cable have been described in a companion volume [TS II]. The attenuation, or loss, of a transmission line increases with increase in frequency but not as rapidly as the wavelength of the signal decreases. Because of this, although the line attenuation per metre will increase with frequency, the loss per wavelength will decrease. Radio-frequency lines are used as *feeders* to connect the radio transmitter to the transmit aerial, and to connect the radio receiver to the receive aerial. R.F. lines are also employed in v.h.f. and u.h.f. equipment to act as components, such as inductors, and as resonant circuits. The lengths of line involved for these applications are generally not large and so the attenuation of a feeder is not always an important factor and may often be neglected.

Lines used as r.f. components are always short in length. A line whose attenuation is negligibly small is often said to be a LOSS-FREE LINE.

Matched Transmission Lines

When a transmission line is employed as a feeder to connect a radio transmitter or a radio receiver to its aerial, it is required to transfer the maximum possible power from its source to its load. This means that the line should be correctly TERMI-NATED, that is, terminated in a resistance that is equal to the CHARACTERISTIC RESISTANCE of the line. Such a line is said to be MATCHED.

Primary Coefficients of a Line

The four primary coefficients of a transmission line are the series resistance and inductance of the conductors, and the capacitance and leakance between the conductors. All four coefficients are uniformly distributed along the length of the line.

The LEAKANCE represents the flow of current through the finite insulation resistance between the conductors and the power dissipated in the dielectric as the line capacitance is alternately charged and discharged. In addition, further losses may occur at the higher radio frequencies if the conductors should radiate energy. A coaxial pair is nearly always operated with its outer conductor earthed and the outer then acts as a screen. The SCREENING effect then reduces very considerably the radiation of energy by a coaxial pair to the outside world and it also ensures that little, if any, externally produced energy can penetrate inside. The efficiency of the screening depends upon the construction of the outer conductor; when a solid copper tube is used, radiation is negligible, if present at all, but when a copper braid forms the outer conductor, as with flexible coaxial cables, the screening efficiency is not as good and decreases with increase in frequency.

Radiation from a balanced two-wire line will occur if the distance between the two conductors is an appreciable fraction of a wavelength; if the two-wires are electrically close together the energy radiated by one wire will cancel out the radiation from the other. This is because at any point along the line the two wires are carrying currents of equal amplitude but of opposite phase, i.e. the current is flowing in one direction in one wire and in the reverse direction in the other wire.

Consider, for example, Fig. 1.2a which shows the current flowing in a line whose conductors are spaced $\lambda/100$ apart. The energy radiated by the bottom conductor is in antiphase with the radiation from the top conductor and, since $\lambda/100$ corresponds to an angle of 3.6°, the two fields almost entirely cancel out. At a much higher frequency the same two conductors may be $\lambda/2$ apart (Fig. 1.2b); now the field radiated by the lower conductor, initially 180° lagging, has a $\lambda/2$ distance to travel before reaching the upper conductor and will have a total phase lag, relative to the field due to the upper conductor, of (180° + 180°) or 360°. This means that at this frequency the

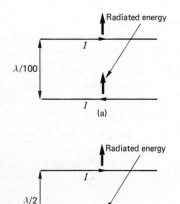

Fig. 1.2 Radiation from a two-wire line

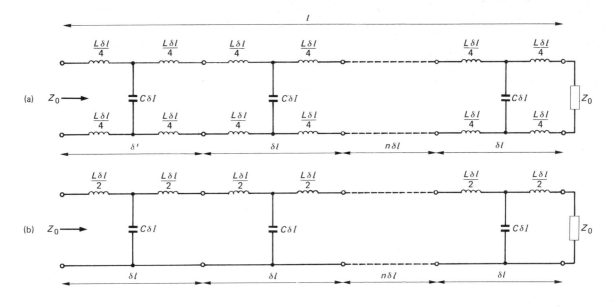

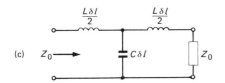

Fig. 1.3 Equivalent circuit of a loss-free line

fields produced by the two conductors are in phase with one another and so do not cancel.

At radio frequencies the attenuation of a line can often be neglected since its magnitude is small for the lengths of line employed. This means that the resistance and the leakance of the line can also be neglected and then the line can be represented by the network given by Fig. 1.3a. The line is considered to consist of a large number of very short lengths, δl, of line connected in cascade as shown. Each short section of line has a total shunt capacitance of $C\delta l$. The series inductance is uniformly distributed along the line and so it is shown in both conductors forming the pair. It is generally more convenient to lump all the inductance into the upper wire as shown in Fig. 1.3b; this does not upset the operation of the line, in theory, since the total series inductance per section is still $L\delta l$.

Secondary Coefficients of a Line

The secondary coefficients of a line determine its performance when a signal at a particular frequency is applied to its sending-end terminals.

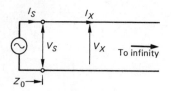

Fig. 1.4 Definition of the characteristic impedance of a line

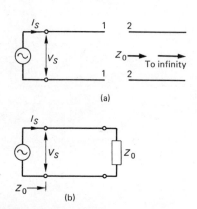

Fig. 1.5 Alternative definition of the characteristic impedance of a line

Characteristic Impedance

The characteristic impedance Z_0 of a transmission line is the input impedance of an infinite length of that line. Fig. 1.4 shows an infinite length of line; its input impedance is the ratio of the voltage V_s applied across the sending-end terminals to the current I_s flowing into the line, i.e.

$$Z_0 = \frac{V_s}{I_s} \tag{1.1}$$

Similarly at any point x along the line the ratio V_x/I_x is always equal to Z_0. Suppose now the line is cut a finite distance from its sending-end terminals as shown in Fig. 1.5a. The remainder of the line is still of infinite length and so the impedance measured at terminals 2-2 is equal to the characteristic impedance. Thus, before the line was cut, terminals 1-1 were effectively terminated in an impedance Z_0. The conditions at the input terminals will not be changed if terminals 1-1 are closed in a physical impedance equal to Z_0, as in Fig. 1.5b.

This leads to a more practical definition: the characteristic impedance of a transmission line is the input impedance of a line that is terminated in the characteristic impedance. A line is said to be CORRECTLY TERMINATED when it is terminated by its characteristic impedance. Thus, when the equivalent circuit of a loss-free line, shown in Figs. 1.3a and b, is terminated in the characteristic impedance Z_0, the impedance measured at the input terminals of the line is also Z_0. Similarly, the input impedance of the second network is also Z_0. This means that the first of the cascaded networks is effectively terminated by Z_0 and so the equivalent circuit of the line can be reduced to the circuit given in Fig. 1.3c. The characteristic impedance of a loss-free transmission line is given by

$$Z_0 = \sqrt{\frac{L}{C}}\ \text{ohms} \tag{1.2}$$

where L and C are the distributed inductance and capacitance per metre.

EXAMPLE 1.1

A radio-frequency transmission line has an inductance of 178.57 nH/m and a capacitance of 71.43 pF/m. Calculate its characteristic impedance.

Solution
From equation (1.2),

$$Z_0 = \sqrt{\frac{178.57 \times 10^{-9}}{71.43 \times 10^{-12}}} = 50\ \Omega \qquad (Ans.)$$

The values of the series inductance and shunt capacitance of a line depend upon the physical dimensions of the line, according to equations (1.3) and (1.4):

for an *air-spaced coaxial line* $Z_0 = 138 \log_{10} \dfrac{R}{r}$ ohms   (1.3)

for a *twin-line* $Z_0 = 276 \log_{10} \dfrac{D}{r}$ ohms   (1.4)

In equation (1.3), R is the inner radius of the outer conductor and r is the radius of the inner conductor, while in equation (1.4) D is the spacing between the centres of the two conductors and r is the radius of each conductor. If either cable employs a continuous insulating material between its conductors, the characteristic impedance is reduced from Z_0 to $Z_0/\sqrt{\varepsilon_r}$, where ε is the relative permittivity of the insulating material.

EXAMPLE 1.2

A twin cable has conductors of 2 mm diameter separated 8 mm from another by continuous solid polythene insulation. If the relative permittivity of the polythene is 2.3, calculate the characteristic impedance of the cable.

Solution
From equation (1.4)

$$Z_0 = \frac{276}{\sqrt{2.3}} \log_{10} \frac{8}{1} = 164.4 \ \Omega \qquad (Ans.)$$

EXAMPLE 1.3

A radio-frequency transmission line has a characteristic impedance of 75 Ω and is connected across the terminals of a signal generator. The signal generator has an internal impedance of 75 Ω and its voltage control is set to give an internal e.m.f. of 10 V. Determine (i) the current which flows into the line and (ii) the voltage across the input terminals of the line. The line is correctly terminated.

Solution
Since the input impedance of a correctly terminated line is Z_0, the conditions at the sending-end of the line can be represented by the circuit of Fig. 1.6.

(i) From Fig. 1.6, $I_s = \dfrac{10}{75+75} = 66.67 \text{ mA}$ (*Ans.*)

(ii) $V_s = I_s Z_0 = 66.67 \times 10^{-3} \times 75 = 5\text{V}$ (*Ans.*)

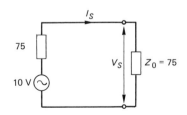

Fig. 1.6

Attenuation Coefficient

As a current or a voltage wave travels along a transmission line it is progressively reduced in amplitude, or attenuated. The ATTENUATION COEFFICIENT α is the attenuation per metre.

The majority of radio-frequency lines are of fairly short length and generally their attenuation is small. Often the line attenuation is sufficiently small for it to be neglected altogether without the introduction of appreciable error. When its attenuation has been neglected a line is said to be *loss-free*; only loss-free lines will be considered in this book.

Phase Change Coefficient

A current (or voltage) wave travels along a line with a finite velocity and so the current (or voltage) at the end of a metre length of line lags the current (or voltage) entering that length. The phase difference between the line current (or voltage) at two points a metre apart is known as the PHASE CHANGE COEFFICIENT β of the line and is measured in radians per metre. The phase change coefficient is a function of the frequency of the signal and both the inductance and capacitance of the line:

$$\beta = \omega \sqrt{(LC)} \text{ rad/s} \tag{1.5}$$

Phase Velocity of Propagation

The PHASE VELOCITY of a line is the velocity with which a sinusoidal wave travels along that line. Any sinusoidal wave travels with a velocity of one wavelength per cycle. There are f cycles per second and so a sinusoidal wave travels with a phase velocity of λf metres per second, i.e.

$$v_p = \lambda f \, m/s \tag{1.6}$$

where λ is the wavelength and f is the frequency of the sinusoidal wave.

In a distance of one wavelength a phase change of 2π radians occurs and so the phase change per metre is $2\pi/\lambda$ radians. Thus

$$\beta = \frac{2\pi}{\lambda} \quad \text{or} \quad \lambda = \frac{2\pi}{\beta}$$

and

$$v_p = \lambda f = \frac{2\pi}{\beta} \times f = \frac{\omega}{\beta}$$

But, from equation (1.6), $\beta = \omega \sqrt{(LC)}$, and therefore

$$v_p = \frac{\omega}{\omega \sqrt{(LC)}} = \frac{1}{\sqrt{(LC)}} \text{ m/s} \tag{1.7}$$

This means that signals at all frequencies are propagated along a loss-free line with the same velocity. The phase velocity will be somewhat less than the velocity of light.

EXAMPLE 1.4

A radio-frequency transmission line has an inductance of 263.2 nH per metre and a capacitance of 46.8 pF per metre. Calculate (i) its characteristic impedance, (ii) its phase change coefficient at 30 MHz, and (iii) its phase velocity of propagation.

Solution.

(i) $Z_0 = \sqrt{\dfrac{L}{C}} = \sqrt{\dfrac{263.2 \times 10^{-9}}{46.8 \times 10^{-12}}} = 75\,\Omega$ (*Ans.*)

(ii) $\beta = \omega\sqrt{(LC)} = 2\pi \times 30 \times 10^6 \times \sqrt{(263.2 \times 10^{-9} \times 46.8 \times 10^{-12})}$
$$= 0.66\ \text{rad/m} = 38°/\text{m} \qquad (Ans.)$$

(iii) $v_p = 1/\sqrt{(LC)} = 1/\sqrt{(263.2 \times 10^{-9} \times 46.8 \times 10^{-12})}$
$$\simeq 2.85 \times 10^8\ \text{m/s} \qquad (Ans.)$$

The phase change coefficient β can be determined using an alternative method:

$$\lambda = \frac{v}{f} = \frac{2.85 \times 10^8}{30 \times 10^6} = 9.5\ \text{m}$$

$$\beta = \frac{2\pi}{\lambda} = \frac{2\pi}{9.5} = 0.66\ \text{rad/m (as before)}$$

Group Velocity of Propagation

When a complex wave is transmitted along a transmission line, each of the component frequencies contained within the wave is propagated with its particular phase velocity. The phase velocity of a radio-frequency transmission line is given by equation (1.7) and is clearly independent of frequency. This means that all the components of a radio-frequency complex wave are propagated along a line with the same velocity and will therefore arrive at the far end of the line at the same time. The GROUP VELOCITY of a radio-frequency line is equal to the common phase velocity of the component frequencies and consequently there is no group delay/frequency distortion (see TS II).

Progression of a Wave along a Line

Consider a loss-free radio-frequency line that is 100 metres in length and is correctly terminated at its far end. Suppose the phase change coefficient at a particular frequency is equal to 4.5° per metre and that a sinusoidal voltage of 1 volt peak value is maintained across its sending-end terminals. Since the line is loss-free the voltage will not be attenuated as it travels along the line but it will experience a progressively increasing phase lag. At a distance of 10 metres from the input terminals the voltage will lag the sending-end voltage by 45°, 20 metres along the line the phase lag will be 90°, and so on for the remainder of the line. The phase lag of the line voltage, relative to the sending-end voltage, at 10 metre intervals along the length of the line is listed in Table 1.1.

Table 1.1

Distance from sending end (m)	Phase lag (°)	Distance from sending end (m)	Phase lag (°)
0	0	60	270
10	45	70	315
20	90	80	360
30	135	90	405
40	180	100	450
50	225		

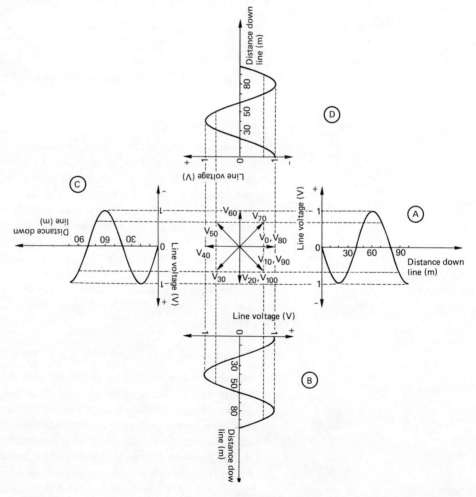

Fig. 1.7 Polar diagram of the voltages along a matched loss-free line

A POLAR DIAGRAM can be drawn to show the magnitude and phase, relative to the sending end, of the voltage as it travels along line. The diagram consists of a series of phasors drawn with the correct length and at the correct angle to represent the line voltages at various points on the line. The polar diagram for the line under consideration is shown in Fig. 1.7.

At the instant when the sending end voltage is zero and is about to go positive, the voltages existing at various distances along the line can be found by projecting from the tips of the various phasors to the corresponding points on axis A; this is shown in the figure by the dotted lines. The waveform showing how the line voltage varies with distance at this particular instant in time is obtained by drawing a smooth curve to join the plotted points. A quarter of a period later the instantaneous value of the input voltage is at its positive peak value of 1 volt. This condition is obtained by rotating the polar diagram in the anticlockwise direction through an angle of 90° and then projecting from the tips of the phasors on to axis B. The phasor representing the sending end voltage is now pointing vertically upwards to indicate maximum positive value. Joining the points plotted in this way on axis B produces the waveform showing how the line voltage varies with distance at this instant in time. The waveforms of the line voltage at the instants in time when the input voltage is, first, zero voltage and about to go negative and, secondly, peak negative voltage, are shown plotted on axes C and D respectively. To obtain waveform C the polar diagram must be rotated in the anticlockwise direction by a further 90°, and then by another 90° for waveform D.

If the four voltage waveforms shown on axes A, B, C, and D in Fig. 1.7 are redrawn beneath one another, as shown by Fig. 1.8, it is possible to see that a particular part of the voltage waveform travels along the line. Consider, for example, the negative peak value of -1 volt; in Fig. 1.8a this value occurs at a point 20 metres from the sending end of the line; in Fig. 1.8b, which shows the line waveform $T/4$ later, where T is the periodic time of the input voltage waveform, the negative peak has moved another 20 metres along the line. Similarly, in each of the following two $T/4$ intervals of time the negative peak of the voltage waveform travels another 20 metres (see Figs. 1.8c and d). The wavelength of the signal is 80 metres. Since the characteristic impedance of a radio-frequency line is purely resistive, the waveform of the current is in phase with the voltage waveform.

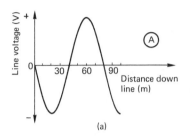

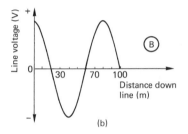

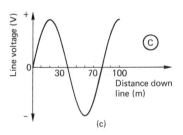

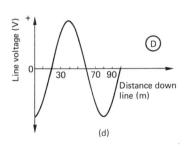

Fig. 1.8 Progression of a voltage wave along a line

Mismatched Transmission Lines

The energy transmitted along a line by the propagating current and voltage waves can be completely dissipated in the terminating load resistance only if that resistance is equal to the characteristic impedance of the line. If the load resistance has some other value, some of the incident energy must be reflected at the load and transmitted back down the line towards the sending end. This means that a fraction of *both* the incident current and the incident voltage is reflected by the load. The voltage (or current) appearing across the load resistance is the phasor sum of the incident and reflected voltages (or currents) at the load. The two extreme values of possible load resistance are an open circuit (infinite impedance) and a short circuit (zero impedance). There can be no current flowing in an open circuit and so there can be no power dissipated. This means that *all* the incident current and voltage are reflected by the open circuit, the current being reflected in antiphase so that the total current at the open-circuit will be zero. Similarly, there can be no voltage developed across a short circuit, and again no power can be dissipated. The current and voltage arriving at the short circuit are both completely reflected, with the voltage experiencing 180° phase shift so that the total voltage across the short circuit will be zero. The reflected current and voltage are propagated towards the sending end of the line, and at any point along the line the total current or voltage is the phasor sum of the incident and reflected waves.

To determine the current and voltage distributions in a resonant line consider a transmission line that is one wavelength long and has its output terminals open-circuited (Fig. 1.9). When the source is first connected to the sending-end terminals of the line, a current equal to the e.m.f. of the source divided by the characteristic impedance of the line, flows into the line. As this current flows along the line it is attenuated and phase shifted. Assume the loss of the line to be negligible and consider the current at points that are multiples of $\lambda/4$ from the sending end. Then, referring to Fig. 1.10 in which the line current is represented by phasors, the current at each point will *lag* the current at the preceding point by 90°. At the end of the line the *incident* current will arrive at the open-circuit. The current flowing in an open-circuit is, of course, zero and therefore all the incident current is *reflected with 180° phase shift*. The reflected current travels back along the line towards the sending end, experiencing the same phase change as the incident current. The phasors representing the reflected current are shown in Fig. 1.11*a*.

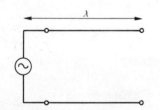

Fig. 1.9 The open-circuited transmission line

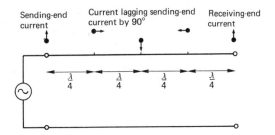

Fig. 1.10 Illustrating transmission of the incident current along a loss-free line one wavelength long

The total line current at each point is the phasor sum of the incident and reflected currents. At the open-circuit the incident and reflected currents are in antiphase and so their phasor sum is zero. A quarter of a wavelength from the open-circuit the two currents are in phase and their phasor sum is equal to twice the incident current. A half-wavelength from the open-circuit the currents are again in antiphase and their phasor sum is again zero, and so on. If the *r.m.s.* values of the total current at each point are plotted the waveform shown in Fig. 1.11*b* is obtained. The points of maximum current, or *antinodes*, always occur at the same points in the line, and so do the points of zero current, or *nodes*. The wave is therefore known as a STANDING WAVE.

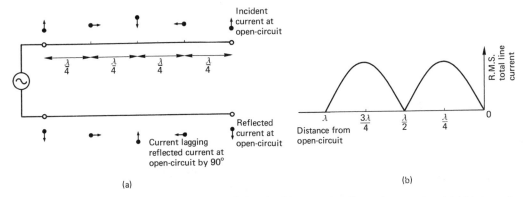

(a)

(b)

Fig. 1.11 (*a*) The incident and reflected currents at λ/4 intervals along a loss-free open-circuited line and (*b*) the r.m.s. value of the total current at each point

If, now, the voltages existing on the line are considered, the phasors shown in Fig. 1.12*a* are obtained. The incident voltage reaching the open-circuited end of the line is completely *reflected with zero phase shift*. At the open-circuit, therefore, the total voltage is twice the incident voltage; at a distance of a quarter-wavelength, the total voltage is zero; and at a distance of a half-wavelength, the total voltage is again twice the

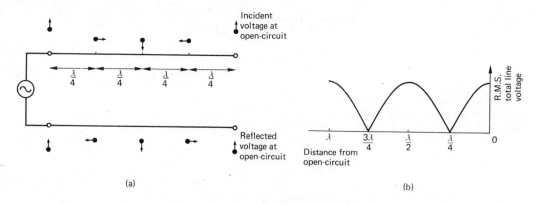

(a)

(b)

Fig. 1.12 (a) The incident and reflected voltages at λ/4 intervals along a loss-free open-circuited line and (b) the r.m.s. value of the total voltage at each point

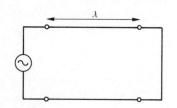

Fig. 1.13 The short-circuited transmission line

incident voltage, and so on. Fig. 1.12b shows the r.m.s. value of the total line voltage plotted against distance from the open-circuit.

Two things should be noted from Figs. 1.11b and 1.12b: the voltage standing-wave pattern is displaced by a quarter-wavelength from the current standing-wave pattern. Secondly, the current and voltage conditions at the open-circuit are repeated at half-wavelength intervals along the line.

Fig. 1.13 shows a length of line that has its output terminals short-circuited. Incident current and voltage waves will flow into the input terminals of the line and will be propagated towards the receiving end. Here both the current and voltage will be totally reflected, the current with zero phase shift and the voltage with a phase change of 180°. This is the inverse of the situation that exists when the terminals are open circuited. Therefore, Fig. 1.11a can also be used to show the phasors representing the incident and reflected voltages on a short-circuited line. Fig. 1.11b shows how the r.m.s. total voltage on a short-circuited line varies with distance from the short circuit. Similarly, Fig. 1.12b shows the variation with distance of the r.m.s. total current on a short-circuited line.

Exercises

1.1. What is meant by the *characteristic impedance* of a transmission line? Give an expression for the characteristic impedance of a radio-frequency loss-free line. A radio-frequency loss-free line has an inductance of $1.2\ \mu H/m$ and a capacitance of $13.32\ pF/m$. Calculate (i) the characteristic impedance and (ii) the phase velocity of propagation of the line. What current will flow if a 10 V source of impedance equal to the characteristic impedance were applied to the input terminals of the line?

1.2. A loss-free transmission line has a characteristic impedance of $600\ \Omega$ and a phase change coefficient of $30°$ per 10 m at a particular frequency. A sinusoidal voltage at this frequency and of 3 V peak value is applied to the input terminals of the line. Use a polar diagram to draw the waveform of the current in the first 120 metres of the line at the instant when the input voltage is zero and about to go positive.

1.3. A loss-free line is $\lambda/4$ long and its output terminals are short-circuited. Draw phasors to represent the currents and voltages on the line and hence draw curves to show how the r.m.s. current and voltage on the line vary with distance from the short circuit. Consider points which are $\lambda/16$ apart.

1.4. What is meant by (i) the characteristic impedance and (ii) the phase change coefficient of a loss-free line? A loss-free line has a characteristic impedance of $500\ \Omega$ and is correctly terminated. At the sending end a current of 1 A flows into the line. Calculate the power dissipated in the load.

1.5. Explain the meanings of the following terms which are used in conjunction with transmission lines: (i) loss-free, (ii) standing wave, (iii) incident wave, (iv) reflected wave (v) incorrectly terminated.

1.6. (*a*) The attenuation of a transmission line increases with increase in frequency, yet the attenuation of a radio-frequency line is often neglected. Discuss why this is so. (*b*) Draw waveforms of the voltage along a matched transmission line that show how a wave progresses from the input terminals to the load.

1.7. Explain the meanings of the following terms used in conjunction with transmission lines: (*a*) characteristic impedance, (*b*) phase change coefficient, (*c*) phase velocity, (*d*) group velocity, and (*e*) standing wave.

1.8. A transmission line has a characteristic impedance of $50\ \Omega$. A 100 metre length of this line has its far end terminals closed by a $50\ \Omega$ resistor. What is the input impedance of the line? What would be the input impedance if the $50\ \Omega$ resistor were removed and the terminals were instead connected to the input terminals of a 25 metre length of another line? The second line has a characteristic impedance of $50\ \Omega$ and is correctly terminated.

1.9. A transmission line has an inductance of $1.5\ \mu H/m$ and a capacitance of $13\ pF/m$. Calculate the characteristic impedance and the phase velocity of propagation of the line.

1.10. A loss-free radio-frequency line has a characteristic impedance of $60\ \Omega$ and a phase velocity of propagation of 2.8×10^8 m/s. Determine its inductance and capacitance per metre.

Short Exercises

1.11. What is meant by the *wavelength* of a signal? In what units is it measured? How does the wavelength of a signal travelling along a line depend upon the inductance and capacitance of the line?

1.12. A line is 10 metres in length. Would you consider this to be an electrically long, or an electrically short line?

1.13 Why are both a two-wire and a coaxial line able to convey energy with little self-radiation?

1.14. Draw the equivalent electrical circuit of a loss-free line. Suggest how line resistance and leakance could be added to your diagram.

1.15. What is meant when it is said that a line is *correctly terminated*? Explain why maximum power is dissipated in the load impedance of a transmission line when the load impedance is equal to the characteristic impedance of the line.

1.16. Make lists of the primary and secondary coefficients of a loss-free radio-frequency transmission line.

1.17. A radio-frequency transmission line has a phase change coefficient of $1.2°$ per metre at a particular frequency. What is the phase difference between the currents at the sending end and receiving end of the line if the line is 10 metres long? What will be the phase difference at a frequency twice as great?

1.18. What is meant by the (i) characteristic impedance, (ii) the input impedance, and (iii) the load impedance of a transmission line? How are these impedances related?

2 Aerials

Introduction

In a radio system, whether for point-to-point communication or for sound and/or television broadcasting, the intelligence signal is used to modulate a radio-frequency carrier wave and the modulated wave is radiated into the atmosphere, in the form of an electromagnetic wave, by a TRANSMITTING AERIAL. For the signal to be received the electromagnetic wave must be intercepted by a RECEIVING AERIAL. The performance of an aerial is the same whether it is used for transmission or for reception, the main difference lying in the magnitudes of the powers involved. The power handled by a transmitting aerial may be very large, perhaps several kilowatts, but the power absorbed by a receiving aerial is very small, possibly only a microwatt or so.

Radiation from an Aerial

Whenever a current flows in a conductor, the conductor is surrounded by a magnetic field, the direction of which is determined by the direction of current flow. If the current changes, the magnetic field will change also. Now, a varying magnetic field *always* produces an electric field that exists *only* while the magnetic field continues to change. When the magnetic field is constant the electric field disappears. The direction of the electric field depends on whether the magnetic field is growing or collapsing and can be determined by the application of Lenz's law. Similarly, a changing electric field *always* produces a magnetic field; this means that a conductor carrying an alternating current is surrounded by continually changing magnetic and electric fields that are completely dependent on one another. Although a stationary electric field can exist without the presence of a magnetic field and vice versa, it is impossible for either field to exist separately when changing.

If a sinusoidal current is flowing in a conductor the electric and magnetic fields around the conductor will also attempt to vary sinusoidally. When the current reverses direction the magnetic field must first collapse into the conductor and *then* build up in the opposite direction. A finite time is required for a magnetic field and its associated electric field to collapse, however, and at frequencies above about 15 kHz not all the energy contained in the field has returned to the conductor before the current has started to increase in the opposite direction and create new electric and magnetic fields. The energy left outside the conductor cannot then return to it and instead, is propagated away from the conductor at the velocity of light (approximately 3×10^8 m/s), see Fig. 2.1. The amount of energy radiated from the conductor increases with increase in frequency, since more energy is then unable to return to the conductor.

The energy radiated from the conductor or aerial, known as the *radiated field*, is in the form of an ELECTROMAGNETIC WAVE in which there is a continual interchange of energy between the electric and magnetic fields. In an electromagnetic wave the electric and magnetic fields are at right angles to each other and they are mutually at right angles to the direction of propagation, as shown in Fig. 2.2 for a particular instant in

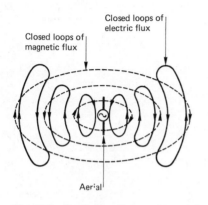

Closed loops of magnetic flux

Closed loops of electric flux

Aerial

Fig. 2.1 Radiation from an aerial

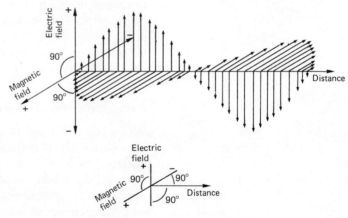

Fig. 2.2 The electromagnetic wave

time. The plane containing the electric field and the direction of propagation of the electromagnetic wave is known as the *plane of polarization* of the wave. For example, if the electric field is in the vertical plane, the magnetic field will be in the horizontal plane, and the wave is said to be vertically polarized. A vertically polarized wave will induce an e.m.f. in any *vertical* conductor that it passes, because its magnetic field will cut the conductor, but will have no effect on any horizontal conductor.

In the immediate vicinity of an aerial the electric and magnetic fields are of greater magnitude and different relative phase than in the radiated field. This is because there is, in addition to the radiated field, an INDUCTION FIELD near the aerial. The induction field represents energy that is not radiated away from the aerial, i.e. the energy that does succeed in returning to the conductor, and its magnitude diminishes inversely as the square of the distance from the aerial. The magnitude of the RADIATED FIELD is proportional to the frequency of the wave and inversely proportional to the distance from the aerial. Near the aerial, the induction field is larger than the radiation field, but the radiation field is the larger at distances greater than $\lambda/2\pi$, where λ is the wavelength of the signal radiated from the aerial.

The amplitudes of the electric field E, and the magnetic field H, in an electromagnetic wave bear a constant relationship to each other. This relationship is known as the *impedance of free space* and is the ratio of the electric field strength to the magnetic field strength, i.e.

$$\text{Impedance of free space} = \frac{E \text{ (volts/metre)}}{H \text{ (ampere-turns/metre)}}$$

$$= 120\pi \text{ ohms} \qquad (2.1)$$

$$= 377 \ \Omega \qquad (2.1a)$$

It is customary to refer to the amplitude of a radio wave in terms of its electric field strength.

EXAMPLE 2.1

The magnetic field strength 10 km from a transmitting aerial is 0.053 At/km. Calculate the electric field strength 50 km from the aerial in the same direction.

Solution

$$E/H = 377 \ \Omega \text{ (from eqn. (2.1a))}$$

or

$$E = 377H = 377 \times 0.053 \simeq 20 \text{ mV/m}$$

At 50 km from the aerial the electric field strength is therefore

$$E = 20/5 = 4 \text{ mV/m} \qquad (Ans.)$$

Current and Voltage Distributions in Aerials

A RESONANT AERIAL is one which is an integral number of wavelengths long, for example the half-wavelength ($\lambda/2$) dipole shown in Fig. 2.3.

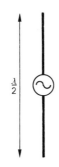

Fig. 2.3 The half-wave dipole

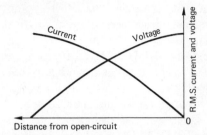

Fig. 2.4 Standing waves of current and voltage on a λ/4 open-circuited loss-free line

The r.m.s. current and voltage distributions on an open-circuited loss-free line that is one wavelength long are shown by Figs. 1.11*b* and 1.12*b* respectively. Using these graphs the standing waves of current and voltage on a λ/4 length are easily obtained and are shown by Fig. 2.4.

Similar standing-wave patterns will result if the two conductors forming the transmission line are each opened out through 90° to form a DIPOLE AERIAL. As the conductors are opened out they will begin to radiate energy, since their separation will be an appreciable fraction of a wavelength and the resultant losses will slightly modify the standing-wave pattern. Since each conductor is a quarter-wavelength long, a λ/2 dipole will be formed. Reference to Fig. 2.4 shows that for a λ/4 length of open-circuited line the current increases from zero at the open-circuit to a maximum, while the voltage falls from its maximum value at the open-circuit to zero at the input terminals. Hence the r.m.s. current and voltage distributions on a λ/2 dipole are as shown in Fig. 2.5*a*. If peak values are considered Fig. 2.5*b* will give the current and voltage distributions.

Fig. 2.5 Current and voltage distributions on a half-wave dipole showing (*a*) r.m.s. values and (*b*) peak values

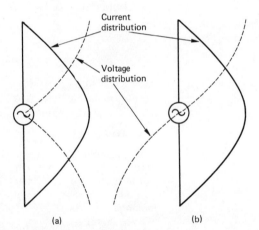

Electrically short aerials are employed at low and medium frequencies where it is impracticable to construct an aerial whose length is comparable with the signal wavelength. For example, a half-wavelength at 300 kHz is 500 m, and at 30 kHz it is 5 km.

In the low and medium wavebands, therefore, transmitting aerials are mounted immediately above the earth, and are fed between the base of the aerial and earth. In such an aerial, whose length is very short compared to the wavelength of the signal, say λ/16 or less, the current distribution is linear as shown in Fig. 2.6.

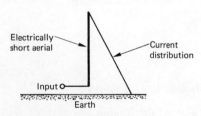

Fig. 2.6 Current distribution on an electrically short aerial

Impedance of an Aerial

Impedance is the ratio of voltage to current. It is evident from the current and voltage distributions shown in Figs. 2.5 and 2.6 that the impedance will vary along the length of an aerial. It is necessary, therefore, to specify the point in the aerial at which the impedance is measured, and usually the input terminals of the aerial are chosen. It would appear from Fig. 2.5 that the input impedance of a centre-fed $\lambda/2$ dipole is zero, since in the middle of the aerial the voltage is zero and the current is a maximum. It should be remembered, however, that Fig. 2.5 is based on the assumption of zero losses; this, of course, is not so, since the aerial radiates power and hence the actual current and voltage distributions are slightly different from those shown. As a result, the input impedance of a dipole is not zero but is approximately 73 Ω. If the physical length of the aerial is exactly a half-wavelength, the input impedance has a small inductive component. To obtain a purely resistive input impedance, a length slightly less than half a wavelength should be used. Sometimes it is more convenient to end-feed a dipole; the input impedance is then high, about 3600 Ω.

If the signal frequency is changed to make the dipole slightly longer than the resonant length, the input impedance is inductive; conversely, if the dipole is less than the resonant length, the input impedance is capacitive. The feed current of the aerial is at its maximum value when the input impedance is purely resistive, and since the energy radiated from the aerial is proportional to the square of the aerial current, the aerial is at its most effective as a radiator when it is resonant.

The reactive component of the input impedance of an aerial is a function of the diameter of the conductor; an increase in diameter reduces the reactance. If an aerial is to handle signals of wide bandwidth its input impedance should have as low a reactive component as possible, and hence a thick conductor should be employed.

Energy must be fed into, or taken away from, an aerial by means of a transmission line known as a *feeder*. If a two-wire feeder is employed it cannot be connected directly to the input terminals of a $\lambda/2$ dipole because considerable mismatch would occur. A two-wire line has a characteristic impedance of a few hundred ohms, and for correct matching the feeder must be connected to a point of higher impedance. Connection between the feeder and the aerial can be made by the method shown in Fig. 2.7a, the tapping points selected being those where the voltage/current ratio is reasonably close to the feeder impedance. If a coaxial feeder is employed it can be connected to the mid-point of the aerial (Fig. 2.7b) because the 75 Ω characteristic impedance of a coaxial feeder is very nearly equal to the 73 Ω aerial input impedance.

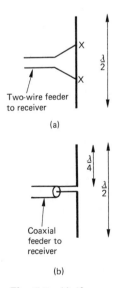

Fig. 2.7 Half-wave dipole fed by (a) two-wire feeder and (b) coaxial feeder

Radiation Patterns, Directivity, and Aerial Gain

All aerials have the property of being able to radiate power better in some directions than in others. The directional characteristic, or DIRECTIVITY, of a transmitting aerial is very useful because it allows most of the transmitted power to be sent in the wanted direction and very little in unwanted directions. This reduces the transmitter power required to produce a given field strength at a distant point in the wanted direction. The directivity of a transmitting aerial is expressed by its RADIATION PATTERN (or polar diagram).

The radiation pattern of an aerial is a graphical representation of the way in which the electric field strength produced by the aerial varies at equal distances from the aerial. Since an aerial radiates energy in all directions, other than along its axis, two radiation patterns are needed to give a reasonable idea of the aerial's performance. The two planes normally chosen are shown in Fig. 2.8; the *meridian* plane contains the axis of the aerial, while the *equatorial* plane is at right angles to the aerial. For example, for a vertical aerial, the meridian plane is vertical and the equatorial plane is horizontal.

A radiation pattern refers to the performance of the aerial itself, i.e. when it is mounted well away from any objects, such as buildings or the earth, which by reflecting signals might affect the shape of the pattern. Since aerials are generally mounted near to some object or other, a radiation pattern does not give a true indication of the performance to be expected from a particular aerial installation. However, a radiation pattern does give a method of comparing different types of aerial.

An aerial may be used for receiving signals as well as transmitting them, and the radiation pattern also gives an indication of the receiving capabilities of the aerial. Directivity in a receiving aerial is useful because it enables the aerial to distinguish, to some extent, between wanted and unwanted signals.

A vertical dipole aerial will radiate, or receive, equally well in all directions in the horizontal plane; hence its horizontal plane radiation pattern is a circle (Fig. 2.9*a*). In the vertical plane such an aerial does not radiate or receive at all in the line of the aerial axis, its vertical plane radiation pattern having a figure-of-eight shape (Fig. 2.9*b*).

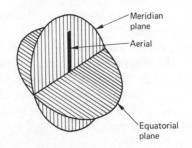

Fig. 2.8 The meridian and equatorial planes of an aerial

Meridian plane

Aerial

Equatorial plane

Front-to-Back Ratio

Many radiation patterns exhibit much greater directivity in one direction than in any other. The FRONT-TO-BACK RATIO

HORIZONTAL: Ae
REVERSED
DIAGRAMS

POLLAR DIAGRAM   RADIAZON PATTERN

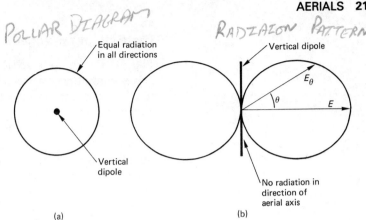

Fig. 2.9 Radiation patterns of a vertical $\lambda/2$ dipole: (a) horizontal plane pattern and (b) vertical plane pattern

(a)   (b)

Fig. 2.10 Front-to-back ratio of an aerial

of an aerial is the ratio of the electric field strengths produced at the same distance from the aerial but in opposite directions. Thus in Fig. 2.10 the front-to-back ratio is E_f/E_b.

EXAMPLE 2.2

The field strength produced x kilometres in the wanted direction from an aerial is $10\,\text{mV/m}$ and at the same distance in the opposite direction it is $1\,\text{mV/m}$. Calculate the front-to-back ratio of the aerial.

Solution

$$\text{Front-to-back ratio} = \frac{E_f}{E_b} = \frac{10 \times 10^{-3}}{1 \times 10^{-3}} = 10 \qquad (Ans.)$$

or, in decibels,

$$\text{Front-to-back ratio} = 20\log_{10} 10 = 20\,\text{dB} \qquad (Ans.)$$

Beamwidth

The BEAMWIDTH of an aerial is a convenient measure of the directivity of the aerial. It is the angle subtended by the points at which the radiation power has fallen to half its maximum value or the field strength has fallen to $1/\sqrt{2}$ of its maximum voltage, i.e. the angle subtended by the 3 dB points on the radiation pattern of the aerial. Thus, in Fig. 2.11, the angle θ is the beamwidth.

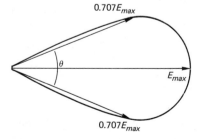

$0.707E_{max}$

E_{max}

$0.707E_{max}$

Fig. 2.11 Beamwidth of an aerial

The Gain of an Aerial

The GAIN OF AN AERIAL is not, as with amplifiers, the power-output/power-input ratio. Instead, the gain of an aerial is a measure of its directional properties and indicates the extent to which radiation is concentrated in a particular direction, or the extent to which the aerial receives signals better from one direction than from all others. Aerial gain is defined relative to a reference aerial and is the same whether the aerial is used for transmission or reception, but may be defined in terms of either.

The GAIN OF A TRANSMITTING AERIAL is the square of the ratio of the field strength produced at a point in the direction of maximum radiation from the aerial to the field strength produced at the same point by the reference aerial, both aerials transmitting the same power. Alternatively, it may be expressed as the ratio of the powers required to be transmitted by the two aerials to produce the same field strength at a particular point in the direction of maximum radiation.

The GAIN OF A RECEIVING AERIAL is the ratio of the power delivered by the aerial to a matched load connected to its terminals to the power delivered by the reference aerial to a matched load, the field strengths at the locations of the aerials being the same.

The reference aerial is either a $\lambda/2$ dipole or an *isotropic radiator*. An isotropic radiator is one which will radiate equally well in all directions. Such an aerial is not a practical possibility but it is a useful concept in more advanced aerial work. It can be shown that the gain of a $\lambda/2$ dipole relative to an isotropic radiator is 1.64 times, or 2.15 dB.

EXAMPLE 2.3

An aerial must be fed with 10 kW of power to produce the same field strength at a given point as a $\lambda/2$ dipole fed with 20 kW of power. Calculate the gain of the aerial (*a*) relative to a $\lambda/2$ dipole, (*b*) relative to an isotropic radiator.

If a modification to the aerial results in the 10 kW input power producing double the field strength at the same point, calculate the new aerial gain relative to a $\lambda/2$ dipole.

Solution

(*a*) Gain of aerial relative to a $\lambda/2$ dipole $= 10 \log_{10} \dfrac{20 \times 10^3}{10 \times 10^3}$

$= 3\,\text{dB}$ (*Ans.*)

(*b*) Gain of $\lambda/2$ dipole relative to an isotropic radiator $= 2.15$ dB. Therefore Gain of aerial relative to isotropic radiator $= 2.15 + 3 = 5.15\,\text{dB}$ (*Ans.*)

The aerial modification doubles the field strength at the point in question, so that

Gain due to modification $= 20 \log_{10} 2 = 6$ dB

and

New gain relative to a $\lambda/2$ dipole $= 3 + 6 = 9$ dB   (*Ans.*)

EXAMPLE 2.4

In a test to determine the gain of an aerial, a standard aerial of known gain is used. Both aerials are situated in a particular field strength and the powers delivered to matched loads are measured. It is found that the power delivered to its load by the aerial under test is $2\,\mu$W and the power delivered by the standard aerial is $8\,\mu$W. If the gain of the standard aerial is 30 dB relative to an isotropic radiator, calculate the gain of the aerial under test.

Solution
Gain of standard aerial relative to aerial under test $=$
$10 \log_{10} \dfrac{8 \times 10^{-6}}{2 \times 10^{-6}} = 6$ dB

Gain of aerial under test relative to isotropic radiator $= 30 - 6 = 24$ dB

Effective Radiated Power

An isotropic radiator is an aerial that is (theoretically) able to radiate energy equally well in all directions, and which therefore produces a constant field strength at a given distance from the aerial in all directions. Any practical aerial does not possess such a radiation characteristic; instead it will concentrate its radiated energy in one or more particular directions. This means that a practical aerial will need to radiate a smaller total power than an isotropic radiator to produce the same field strength at a particular point in the direction of maximum radiation. The EFFECTIVE RADIATED POWER, e.r.p., of an aerial is the power that an isotropic radiator would have to radiate to produce the same field strength at a particular point in the direction of maximum radiation. Numerically, the effective radiated power of an aerial is equal to the product of the total transmitted power P_t and the gain G of the aerial, i.e.

$$\text{e.r.p.} = P_t G \tag{2.2}$$

EXAMPLE 2.5

An aerial with a gain of 10 dB relative to an isotropic radiator radiates a power of 1000 watts. Determine the effective radiated power of the aerial.

Solution
10 dB is a power ratio of 10:1
Therefore, from equation (2.2),

$$\text{e.r.p.} = 10 \times 1000 = 10 \text{ kW} \quad (\textit{Ans.})$$

Bandwidth

The BANDWIDTH of an aerial is the band of frequencies over which its operation can be considered to be satisfactory. Unfortunately, the satisfactory performance of an aerial can be specified in more than one way but in this book it will be taken as referring to the main lobe of the radiation pattern. For many aerials, maximum radiation in the wanted direction takes place when the lengths and/or spacings of the elements making up the aerial are particular sub-multiples of the signal wavelength. If the frequency is varied the critical dimensions are no longer correct and the radiation in the wanted direction is reduced. Then, the bandwidth of an aerial is the band of frequencies over which the power radiated by the aerial in the wanted direction is not more than 3 dB down on the maximum radiation.

Radiation Resistance and Aerial Efficiency

It is often convenient in aerial work to regard the power radiated from an aerial as being dissipated in a fictitious resistance, known as the *radiation resistance*. The power radiated from an aerial is then given by

$$\text{Power radiated} = I^2 R_r \tag{2.3}$$

where I is the current fed into the aerial and R_r is the radiation resistance.

The radiation resistance of a $\lambda/2$ dipole is equal to its impedance, i.e. 73 Ω, while the radiation resistance of an electrically short aerial, say $\lambda/50$, is only about 0.1 Ω.

The power radiated from an aerial is always less than the power fed into it because some power is lost in the aerial. Sources of power loss are I^2R losses in the aerial conductor and in the ground adjacent to the aerial, corona losses and dielectric losses in insulators. The aerial losses can be lumped together and represented by a *loss resistance R_L*, in which all the lost power is assumed to be dissipated.

The efficiency η of an aerial is the ratio of the power radiated to the power fed to the aerial, usually expressed as a percentage:

$$\eta = \frac{I^2 R_r}{I^2 R_L + I^2 R_r} = \frac{R_r}{R_L + R_r} \times 100\% \tag{2.4}$$

EXAMPLE 2.6

A low-frequency transmitting aerial has a radiation resistance of 0.3 Ω and a loss resistance of 1.5 Ω. If the current fed into the aerial is 50 A, calculate the radiated power, the power input and the aerial efficiency.

Solution

$$\text{Power radiated} = I^2 R_r = 50^2 \times 0.3 = 750 \text{ W} \qquad (Ans.)$$

$$\text{Input power} = I^2 R_r + I^2 R_L$$
$$= (50^2 \times 0.3) + (50^2 \times 1.5) = 4500 \text{ W} \qquad (Ans.)$$

$$\text{Aerial efficiency} = \frac{100 R_r}{R_L + R_r} = \frac{100 \times 0.3}{0.3 + 1.5} = 16.67\% \qquad (Ans.)$$

At very low frequencies, aerial efficiencies may be only a few per cent, but at very high frequencies, efficiencies greater than 90% can be obtained.

Monopole Aerials

Transmitting aerials operating at frequencies in the very-low, low, and medium bands must employ structures of considerable height and be mounted vertically upon the earth, because at these frequencies the wavelength of the signal is long. It is possible at the upper end of the low-frequency band, and in the medium band, to employ aerials which are λ/4 in length, but often for economic reasons somewhat shorter masts are used.

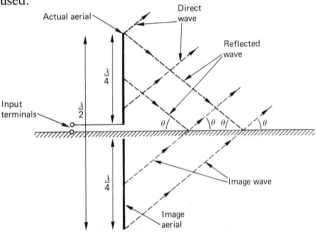

Fig. 2.12 Monopole or unipole aerial

Fig. 2.12 shows a λ/4 aerial that is mounted on the earth's surface and is fed at the bottom between the aerial and the earth. Such an aerial is known as a *unipole* or MONOPOLE. The aerial will radiate energy equally well in all directions in the horizontal plane. In the vertical plane some energy is radiated towards the sky and some is directed downwards towards the earth, as shown by the dotted lines. The downward-directed waves strike the earth and are reflected, provided the earth is flat, with equal angles of incidence and reflection.

At a point distant from the aerial, energy is received by means of both the direct wave and the wave that has been reflected from the earth. The field strength produced at this point is the resultant of the individual field strengths produced by the two waves. From the point of view of an observer located at the distant point, it appears as though the reflected wave has originated from an extension of the aerial beneath the earth. In the diagram this apparent extra length of aerial has been labelled as the *image aerial*. This means that, electrically, the aerial is operating as though its height was twice as great as it actually is. The effective increase in the height of the aerial is advantageous because the field strength produced by an aerial at a given point is proportional to the height of that aerial. The total height of the aerial and its image is $\lambda/2$ and so the current and voltage distributions on the aerial are the same as those on the $\lambda/2$ dipole illustrated by Fig. 2.5. The input impedance of the aerial is purely resistive and is equal to 37 ohms.

The current standing wave pattern results in the existence of a current maximum at the earthed end of the aerial. As a result large currents will flow in the earth in the vicinity of the aerial and will dissipate power. To minimize such power losses, and so keep the aerial efficiency at as high a figure as possible, the earth should be of high conductivity. To ensure this it is usually necessary to instal a network of radial conductors buried beneath the surface of the earth to a depth of about one third of a metre. The network should extend around the aerial for a distance about equal to the height of the aerial. If the earth is too rocky or too sandy near the aerial a *counterpoise* earth may well be employed. A counterpoise earth consists of a network of radial copper conductors that is supported on low-permittivity, insulated poles at a height of about two metres above the surface of the earth.

At low frequencies the aerial height needed to make an aerial $\lambda/4$ long is too large to be economically worthwhile. The use of an electrically short aerial results in the input impedance of the aerial possessing a capacitive component, in a reduction in the radiation resistance of the aerial, and in a reduction in the aerial current (the current in a tuned circuit is a maximum at resonance). The aerial can be tuned to be resonant by the addition of a suitable inductance in series with its input terminals. Unfortunately, the maximum value of the aerial current is now found to exist in the series inductance and not in the aerial itself. Because of this the transmitted power is not as great as might be anticipated.

Effective Height

The current flowing in an aerial is not of uniform amplitude at all points along the aerial but varies for example as shown for two particular aerials in Figs. 2.5 and 2.6.

The EFFECTIVE HEIGHT or EFFECTIVE LENGTH of a transmitting aerial is that length which, if it carried a uniform current having the same magnitude as the input current of the aerial, would produce the same field strength at a given point. This means that the product of the actual height of the aerial and the mean value of the current flowing must be equal to the product of the effective length and the uniform current. That is

$$l_{phys} I_{mean} = l_{eff} I$$

or

$$l_{eff} = \frac{l_{phys} I_{mean}}{I} \qquad (2.5)$$

In the case of an electrically short aerial in which the aerial current varies linearly from a maximum value of I amperes at the base to zero at the top, the mean aerial current is $I/2$. Hence, from equation (2.5),

$$l_{eff} = \tfrac{1}{2} l_{phys}$$

Since the apparent height of an earthed monopole is twice its physical height, because of earth reflections, its effective height is equal to its physical height.

EXAMPLE 2.7

An electrically short aerial that is mounted normal to perfectly conducting earth is 100 m high and carries a current that varies linearly from a maximum of 10 A at the base to 0 A at the top. Determine the effective height of the aerial.

Solution
From equation (2.5), the effective height of the aerial is $(100 \times 5)/10$ or 50 m, but since the aerial is mounted on perfectly conducting earth the effective height is doubled. Therefore

Effective height = 100 metres   (*Ans.*)

The effective height of a receiving aerial is also an important parameter since the e.m.f. induced into the aerial by an incident electromagnetic wave is given by

$$e = E l_{eff} \qquad (2.6)$$

where E is the electric field strength of the wave in V/m.

Hence the voltage induced into a receiving aerial is directly proportional to the electric field strength.

EXAMPLE 2.8

An aerial of effective length 1 m is situated in a field strength of 10 mV/m. Calculate the voltage induced into the aerial.

Solution
$$e = 1 \times 10 \times 10^{-3} = 10 \text{ mV} \qquad (\textit{Ans.})$$

If the mean value of the aerial current could be increased without a corresponding increase in the current at the input terminals, the effective height of the aerial would be increased by the same ratio. This, in turn, would mean that the radiation resistance of the aerial would be higher and more power would be transmitted. The ratio I_{mean}/I of the mean to input aerial currents could be improved if the current could be prevented from falling to zero at the top of the aerial. This is the function of a CAPACITANCE TOP. A horizontal conductor, or system of conductors, is fitted to the top of the aerial and has a relatively large capacitance to earth. Current will now flow in the capacitance top as well as in the aerial and so the aerial current does not fall to zero at the top of the aerial (see Fig. 2.13). The capacitance top can also be provided by means of a horizontal conductor which is suspended between the top of the aerial and one, or two, posts. Two examples of this type of capacitance top are known as the inverted-L and the T aerials.

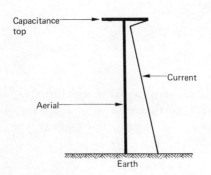

Fig. 2.13 The use of a capacitance top

The Inverted-L Aerial

The *inverted-L aerial* is designed to transmit and/or receive low- and medium-frequency vertically-polarized signals, and the construction of a receive aerial is shown in Fig. 2.14. The aerial proper in which e.m.f.s are induced is the

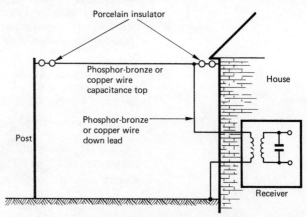

Fig. 2.14 The inverted-L aerial

downlead, and this is much less than $\lambda/2$ in length. The downlead must be cut by the horizontal magnetic field of the incident electromagnetic wave, and it should be as nearly vertical as possible. No e.m.f. is induced in the long horizontal section of the aerial, which is provided to increase the effective length of the aerial and thereby increase the mean aerial current.

The equatorial radiation pattern of an inverted-L aerial is shown in Fig. 2.15, and it can be seen that the aerial exhibits

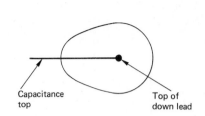

Fig. 2.15 The equatorial plane pattern of an inverted-L aerial

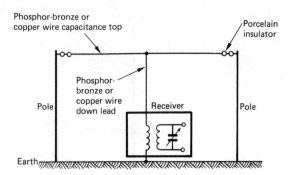

Fig. 2.16 The T aerial

slight directivity, receiving or transmitting somewhat better in the direction from capacitance top to downlead.

For the best results the aerial should be mounted as high as possible and be well clear of buildings that might reduce the field strength of the signals to be received. This type of aerial can be used for domestic radio installations and is ideal when reception of distant stations is required.

The T Aerial

For some installations it may be more convenient to have the downlead connected to the centre of the capacitance top, as shown in Fig. 2.16. Such an arrangement, known as a *T aerial* because of its appearance, is employed, for example, on board a ship. The T aerial transmits or receives equally well in all directions in the horizontal plane and so its equatorial radiation pattern is a circle.

Reflectors and Directors

At v.h.f. and at u.h.f. the wavelength of a signal is fairly short and half-wavelength elements can be used. The equatorial plane radiation pattern of a $\lambda/2$ dipole is a circle, which means that the aerial will receive or radiate equally well from or to all directions in this plane. The meridian plane pattern is a figure-of-eight. The gain and directivity of a $\lambda/2$ dipole can be increased by the addition of a *reflector* and one or more *directors*. Reflectors and directors are both known as *parasitic* elements since neither is directly connected to the aerial feeder.

A REFLECTOR is usually about 5% longer than $\lambda/2$ and it is mounted in the position shown in Fig. 2.17*a*. Consider a radio wave travelling towards the aerial from the direction shown. As the wave travels past the dipole it will induce an e.m.f. into it. In passing on to the reflector the radio wave suffers a phase lag, the magnitude of which depends upon the

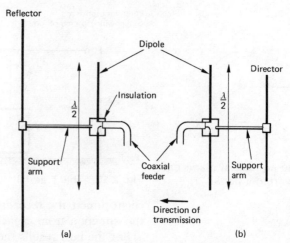

Fig. 2.17 Half-wave dipole with (a) a reflector and (b) a director

spacing between the dipole and the reflector, e.g. if the spacing is 0.15λ the phase lag is 0.15×360° = 54°. The radio wave induces an e.m.f. into the reflector and this causes a current to flow; the reflector current lags the induced e.m.f. because the longer than λ/2 element has an inductive impedance. The reflector re-radiates energy, some of which is directed towards the dipole. By the time the radiated energy reaches the dipole, a further phase lag will have been experienced. If *both* the reflector length *and* the element spacing have been correctly chosen, the energy radiated by the reflector will arrive at the dipole *in phase* with the energy received from the transmitter. The total field strength at the dipole will then be increased; this means that the gain of the aerial in this direction will have been improved. When a radio wave arrives at the aerial from the opposite direction, it will reach the reflector before it reaches the dipole. Voltages will be induced into both elements by the incident wave. A lagging current will flow in the reflector and it will radiate energy towards the dipole. Now, the re-radiated energy arrives at the dipole with such a phase that it reduces the total field strength.

Usually, the dipole-reflector spacing is somewhere between 0.15λ and 0.25λ as a suitable compromise between the conflicting requirements of maximum gain in the wanted direction and maximum front-to-back ratio. The radiation pattern of a λ/2 dipole and a reflector is as shown, in the equatorial and meridian planes by Figs. 2.18a and b respectively.

A DIRECTOR is a parasitic element, cut to a shorter length than λ/2 at the operating frequency, and mounted in front of the dipole (Fig. 2.17b). The action of the director is similar to that of the reflector. Since the length of the director is shorter than λ/2 its impedance is capacitive and an e.m.f. induced by an incident radio wave will produce a leading current. The effect of the director is to assist the action of the reflector and still further increase the gain of the aerial in the wanted

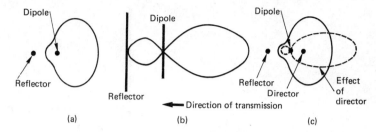

Fig. 2.18 Radiation patterns, (a) λ/2 dipole and reflector: in equatorial plane, (b) λ/2 dipole and reflector: in meridian plane, (c) λ/2 dipole, reflector and director; in equatorial plane

direction. Fig. 2.18c shows the effect on the equatorial plane pattern of adding a director to a dipole-reflector array; obviously there is an increase in the directivity of the aerial. The spacing between the dipole and the director is usually somewhere in the range of values 0.1λ to 0.15λ.

EXAMPLE 2.9

An aerial array consists of a vertical half-wave dipole with a reflector and one director. Calculate approximate dimensions and spacings for the elements if operation is to be at 100 MHz.

Solution
At 100 MHz,

$$\lambda = \frac{3 \times 10^8}{100 \times 10^6} = 3\text{m} \quad \text{and} \quad \frac{\lambda}{2} = 1.5\text{m}$$

In practice, the dipole would be made slightly shorter because the electric field fringes out at each end of the dipole making its length effectively greater. Generally, about 5% is allowed. Therefore

Approximate length of dipole = 1.48 m   (*Ans.*)

The reflector should be about 5% longer than λ/2 and should be 0.15–0.25λ behind the dipole. Therefore

Approximate reflector length = 1.57 m

and

Approximate dipole/reflector spacing = 0.6 m   (*Ans.*)

The director should be about 5% shorter than λ/2, i.e. about 1.43 m   (*Ans.*)

The dipole/director spacing should be 0.1 – 0.15λ, i.e.

Approximate spacing = 0.4 m   (*Ans.*)

A progressive increase in gain can be achieved by adding director elements, each extra director being slightly shorter than the previous one. A typical multi-element dipole aerial is shown in Fig. 2.19.

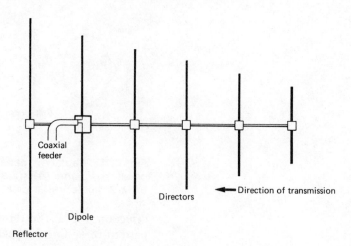

Coaxial
feeder

Directors

Direction of transmission

Dipole

Reflector

Fig. 2.19 A multi-element λ/2 dipole aerial—a Yagi aerial

A limitation of aerials which utilize a dipole and a number of parasitic elements is that their correct operation depends upon the choice of element lengths and spacings (in fractions of the signal wavelength). This means that the satisfactory operation of the aerial is restricted to a narrow band of frequencies centred on the design frequency.

Measurement of Radiation Patterns

The radiation pattern of a particular aerial is the same for both transmission and reception, and in practice, therefore, the more convenient one is measured.

One method of measuring the horizontal plane radiation pattern of a vertical aerial is as follows. The aerial is mounted on a test rig that can be rotated through 360° and placed in a position well clear of any obstructing or reflecting surfaces. The output terminals of the aerial are then connected to the input of a radio receiver, the output of the receiver is fed to a voltmeter that has been calibrated to indicate electric field strength directly. Another, distant aerial is then fed with a constant power at constant frequency and provides the test signal. The aerial under test is then rotated in a number of convenient steps and the indicated field strength at each step is noted, the gain of the receiver remaining unaltered. The results obtained are then plotted to give the radiation pattern of the aerial.

If the aerial to be tested is too large to be rotated, an alternative method of measurement is called for. One possibility is to connect the aerial to a radio transmitter and measure the field strength produced around the aerial. This method necessitates transporting a field-strength measurement equipment around the aerial, at a constant distance from it and obviously introduces some practical difficulties.

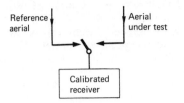

Fig. 2.20 Measurement of aerial gain

Measurement of Aerial Gain

The measurement arrangement is shown in Fig. 2.20, both aerials being located in the constant field strength produced by a distant transmitting aerial. The receiver is first connected to the reference aerial and the output voltage of the receiver is noted. The receiver is then connected to the aerial under test and the new output voltage recorded. The gain of the tested aerial, relative to the reference aerial, is then given by the ratio of the two output voltages. The reference aerial may be either a $\lambda/2$ dipole or some other aerial whose gain is already known.

EXAMPLE 2.10

In an aerial gain measurement the output voltages of a receiver connected in turn to the reference and tested aerials were 1.6 V and 6.4 V respectively. If the reference aerial has a gain of 10 dB relative to a $\lambda/2$ dipole, calculate the gain of the aerial under test.

Solution

$$\text{Gain relative to reference} = 20 \log_{10} \frac{6.4}{1.6} = 20 \log_{10} 4$$

$$= 20 \times 0.6 = 12 \text{ dB}$$

Therefore gain relative to $\lambda/2$ dipole $= 12 + 10 = 22$ dB   (*Ans.*)

Exercises

2.1. What is meant by the term *isotropic radiator?* Draw radiation patterns in the horizontal plane for the following: (*a*) a vertical half-wave dipole aerial, (*b*) a horizontal half-wave dipole aerial, (*c*) a vertical half-wave dipole aerial with reflector, (*d*) a horizontal half-wave dipole aerial with reflector.

Calculate suitable dimensions for an array comprising a half-wave dipole and reflector for use at 559.25 MHz.

2.2. Briefly explain the following terms in connection with aerials: *isotropic aerial, forward gain, beamwidth.* Sketch with approximate scales a radiation pattern in the horizontal plane for a vertical quarter-wave dipole aerial and reflector. Show how this diagram indicates the forward gain and beamwidth of the array.

A resonant dipole aerial is designed to radiate at a particular frequency. Discuss its effectiveness as a radiator at other frequencies.   (*C & G*)

2.3. Sketch the radiation patterns, in the horizontal plane, of the following types of aerial: (*a*) a horizontal dipole, (*b*) a half-wave vertical dipole with reflector, (*c*) an inverted-L, (*d*) a ferrite rod as used in a portable broadcast receiver.

Sketch and explain the construction, including the lead-in to the receiver, of either (i) an inverted-L aerial for the reception of medium-wave signals, or (ii) a dipole and reflector type of aerial commonly used for the reception of television signals.   (*C & G*)

2.4. Explain carefully what is meant by the *radiation pattern of an aerial array.*

Give a dimensioned sketch of a dipole aerial with director

and reflector elements suitable for the reception of 95 MHz broadcast transmissions.

With the aid of a radiation diagram, briefly explain why in urban areas subject to heavy man-made interference, it is sometimes advantageous to offset the axis of the receiving aerial away from the direct line between the transmitting station and the receiving station. *(C & G)*

2.5. Explain the terms (*a*) radiation resistance, (*b*) isotropic radiator, (*c*) aerial efficiency.

An aerial array for use at 805 MHz consists of a vertical half-wave dipole with a reflector and one director. Calculate approximate dimensions and spacings. Sketch the radiation pattern of the array in the horizontal plane.

2.6. Sketch the distribution of current and voltage along a half-wave dipole in free space and explain briefly how this distribution arises. Hence demonstrate that the aerial presents a low impedance to the feeder.

A dipole aerial requires to be fed with 20 kW of power to produce a given signal strength at a particular distant point. If the addition of a reflector makes the same field strength available with an input of only 11 kW, what is the gain in decibels obtained by the use of the reflector? *(C & G)*

2.7. Sketch the radiation patterns of a half-wave vertical dipole in free space, in the vertical and horizontal planes.

Illustrate the influence of (*a*) a reflector, and (*b*) a director on the radiation patterns in the horizontal plane only.

Describe an aerial array using dipole elements as radiators. Define directivity gain and half-power bandwidth. *(C & G)*

2.8. Sketch the vertical radiation pattern of a vertical half-wave dipole in free space and explain in simple terms how this radiation pattern is produced. Describe the action of a conducting rod operating as a reflector placed one-quarter wavelength behind the dipole.

Explain how a unipole aerial functions in relation to a half-wave dipole. Sketch its radiation pattern and give an approximate value of input impedance at the aerial terminals.

(C & G)

2.9. (*a*) Describe the operation of an aerial suitable for use in long-distance low-frequency radio communication. (*b*) Describe the feeder between the aerial in (*a*) and the associated communication equipment. (*c*) Explain the terms *forward gain* and *beamwidth* as applied to aerials. *(C & G)*

2.10. (*a*) With the aid of a diagram describe the principle of operation of a unipole aerial and sketch its radiation pattern. (*b*) Explain any similarity between the unipole aerial and the dipole aerial. (*c*) State one application of the unipole aerial. *(C & G)*

2.11. Explain, with the aid of diagrams, five of the following terms used in relation to aerials: (i) isotropic radiator, (ii) $\lambda/2$ dipole, (iii) unipole, (iv) radiation pattern, (v) aerial gain, (vi) half-power bandwidth. *(C & G)*

2.12. (*a*) Describe the construction of an aerial array consisting of a horizontal dipole, reflector and director, which is suitable for use at signal frequencies of about 90 MHz. (*b*) State, in metres, suitable dimensions for the elements used, (*c*) Illustrate the actions of the reflector and director by sketching the horizontal pattern of (i) the dipole alone, (ii) the dipole with reflector, (iii) the complete array. *(C & G)*

2.13. Why are aerials designed for use at v.h.f. generally more efficient than low-frequency aerials? Write down an expression for the efficiency of an aerial and state the meaning of each symbol used. Sketch an earthed monopole which has a height of $\lambda/8$ at the operating frequency and say why its apparent height is greater than this value. What is meant by a *counterpoise earth* and why is it employed?

2.14. What is meant by saying that an aerial has an efficiency of 10%?

An aerial has a loss resistance of 2.5Ω and a radiation resistance of 1.8Ω. If the current fed into the aerial has a r.m.s. value of 10 A calculate the power radiated by the aerial and the aerial efficiency.

2.15. Describe how radiation of energy from a conductor which is carrying a radio-frequency current takes place. What is meant by the polarization of the wave?

A particular aerial radiates 8 kW power when the power supplied by the feeder is 10 kW. What is the efficiency of the aerial? If the aerial has a gain of 8 dB what is the effective radiated power?

2.16. A dipole aerial must be fed with 20 kW power in order to produce an electric field strength of 5 mV/m at a particular point. The addition of a reflector and a director to the aerial enables the same field strength to be produced by a power of 8 kW. What is the gain, in dB, of the array relative to the dipole alone?

2.17. Sketch, and explain, with the aid of a diagram showing phasors of current and voltage along a length of loss-free line open-circuited at the far end, the current and voltage distributions on a $\lambda/2$ dipole.

Short Exercises

2.18. When an aerial radiates a power of 5 kW a field strength of 5 mV/m is set up at a distant point. Another aerial located at the same site needs to radiate 10 kW to produce the same field strength at the same point. If the first aerial has a gain of 10 dB relative to an isotropic radiator, determine the gain of the second aerial.

2.19. Describe the way in which energy is radiated from a conductor carrying a high-frequency current.

2.20. What is meant by the polarization of a radio wave? In which units is field strength generally measured?

2.21. Distinguish between the induction field and the radiation field of an aerial. Why does a transmitting aerial work more efficiently as the frequency of the exciting current is increased?

2.22. Sketch the radiation pattern of a vertical $\lambda/2$ dipole in both the horizontal and vertical planes. Explain what information these patterns give.

2.23. Define the gain of an aerial in terms of an isotropic radiator. What is an isotropic radiator?

2.24. Why is there a need to tune a practical unipole aerial? What is the purpose of the capacitance top?

2.25. What is meant by the effective height of an aerial? What effect does the earth have on the effective height of a monopole aerial?

2.26. A monopole aerial is 75 metres in height and is mounted vertically on perfectly conducting earth. The aerial current varies linearly from 20 A at the base of the aerial to 0 A at the top. Calculate the effective height of the aerial.

3 The Propagation of Radio Waves

Introduction

If radio-frequency power is fed into a transmitting aerial, electromagnetic energy at the same frequency will be radiated from the aerial. This energy is propagated away from the aerial in a number of directions as predicted by the radiation pattern of the aerial. The radiated energy may reach the receiving aerial by one or more of three main modes of propagation, namely the *surface or ground wave*, the *sky wave* and the *space wave* (Fig. 3.1).

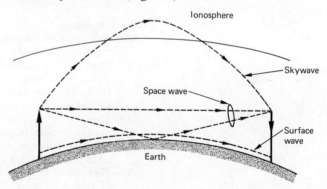

Fig. 3.1 Modes of propagation

The SURFACE WAVE is supported at its lower edge by the surface of the earth, and therefore follows the curvature of the earth as it travels. The SKY WAVE is directed upwards from the earth into the atmosphere, where, under certain conditions, it may be returned to earth. The SPACE WAVE may be considered to consist of two rays, one travelling in a straight line between two points and the other travelling between the same two points by means of a single reflection from the earth.

The ground wave is employed for world-wide communications in the very-low-frequency and low-frequency bands [see

TS II for frequency-band classification], and for sound broadcasting in the medium waveband. The sky wave is used for long-distance telephony links, and the space wave is used for sound broadcasting, for television broadcasting, for land mobile systems, and for multichannel radio-relay systems. In the high-frequency band a transmitting aerial may radiate one, two or all three kinds of wave simultaneously, but generally only one mode is of practical importance in a particular frequency band, and in this chapter the modes will be treated separately. Further, although divergent radio *waves* are propagated, it will be assumed that propagation is by means of narrow *rays*.

The Ground or Surface Wave

The ground wave is the resultant of the space wave and the surface wave, but at low and medium frequencies the height of the transmitting aerial is small compared with the signal wavelength, and the direct and reflected components of the space wave completely cancel. The ground wave is then identical with the surface wave.

The surface or ground wave is one which leaves the transmitting aerial very nearly parallel to the ground. Vertically polarized waves must be used because horizontal polarization would result in the low resistance of the earth short-circuiting the electric component of the wave. The surface wave follows the curvature of the earth as it travels from the transmitter because it is *diffracted*.† Further bending of the wave occurs because the magnetic component of the wave cuts the earth's surface as it travels and induces e.m.f.s in it. The induced e.m.f.s cause alternating currents to flow and dissipate power in the resistance of the earth. This power can only be supplied by the surface wave, and so a continuous flow of energy from the wave into the earth takes place.

The signal wavefront, therefore, has two components of velocity, one in the forward direction and one downwards towards the earth. The resultant direction is the phasor sum of the forward and downward components, and this results in the wave being tilted forward, as shown in Fig. 3.2. The downward component is always normal to the earth and the forward component 90° advanced; hence the tilted wavefront follows the undulations of the ground (Fig. 3.3).

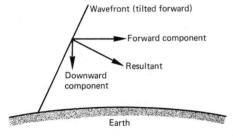

Fig. 3.2 Wavefront of surface wave

---

† Diffraction is a phenomenon, which occurs with all wave motion, that causes a wave to bend around any obstacle it passes. For a surface wave the earth itself is the obstacle.

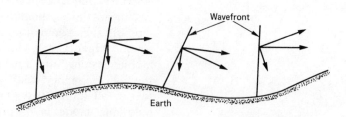

Fig. 3.3 Propagation of surface wave over undulating terrain

The transfer of energy from the wave to the ground attenuates the wave as it travels, and the field strength E_d, at a distance d metres from the transmitter is given by

$$E_d = K \frac{E_1}{d} \tag{3.1}$$

where E_1 is the field strength 1 km from the transmitter and K is the factor representing the wave attenuation caused by the power dissipated in the ground.

The attenuation factor K depends upon the frequency of the wave, and the conductivity and permittivity of the earth. The attenuation at a given frequency is least for propagation over expanses of water and greatest for propagation over dry ground, such as desert. For propagation over ground of average dampness, with a radiated power of 1 kW, the distance giving a field strength of 1 mV/m varies approximately with frequency as shown in Table 3.1.

Table 3.1

Frequency	Range (km)
100 kHz	200
1 MHz	60
10 MHz	6
110 MHz	1.5

The Sky Wave

In the high-frequency band, directive aerials are used which propagate most of the radiated energy towards the sky. In a part of the sky known as the IONOSPHERE the *sky wave* is refracted, and if the conditions are correct, may be returned to earth.

Refraction of an Electromagnetic Wave

When an electromagnetic wave travelling in one medium passes into a different medium its direction of travel will probably be altered. The wave is said to be REFRACTED.

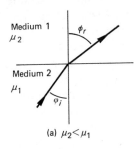

(a) $\mu_2 < \mu_1$

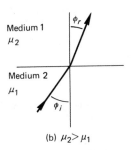

(b) $\mu_2 > \mu_1$

Fig. 3.4 Refraction of electromagnetic waves, (*a*) Wave passing into a medium of lower absolute refractive index, (*b*) Wave passing into a medium of higher absolute refractive index

Fig. 3.5 Refraction of an electromagnetic wave passing through media of progressively lower absolute refractive index

The ratio

$$\frac{\text{sine of angle of incidence } \phi_i}{\text{sine of angle of refraction } \phi_r}$$

is a constant for a given pair of media and is known as the *refractive index* for the media. If one of the two media is air† the *absolute refractive index* of the other medium is obtained.

If a wave passes from one medium to another medium that has a lower absolute refractive index, the wave is bent away from the normal (Fig. 3.4*a*). Conversely, if the wave travels into a region of higher absolute refractive index, the wave is bent towards the normal (Fig. 3.4*b*).

Suppose a wave is transmitted through a number of thin parallel strips (Fig. 3.5), each strip having an absolute refractive index lower than that of the strip immediately below it. The wave will pass from higher to lower absolute refractive index each time it crosses the boundary between two strips, and it is therefore progressively bent *away* from the normal. If the width of the strips is made extremely small, the absolute refractive index will steadily decrease and the wave will be continuously refracted.

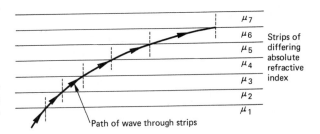

Path of wave through strips

The Ionosphere

Ultra-violet radiation from the sun entering the atmosphere of the earth supplies energy to the gas molecules of the atmosphere. This energy is sufficient to produce ionization of the molecules, that is, remove some electrons from their parent atoms. Each atom losing an electron in this way has a resultant positive charge and is said to be IONIZED.

The ionization thus produced is measured in terms of the number of free electrons per cubic metre and is dependent upon the intensity of the ultra-violet radiation. As the radiation travels towards the earth, energy is continually extracted from it and so its intensity is progressively reduced.

† Strictly speaking, a vacuum.

The liberated electrons are free to wander at random in the atmosphere and in so doing may well come close enough to a positive ion to be attracted to it. When this happens the free electron and the ion recombine to form a neutral atom. Thus a continuous process of ionization and recombination takes place. At high altitudes the atmosphere is rare and little ionization takes place. Nearer the earth the number of gas molecules per cubic metre is much greater and large numbers of atoms are ionized; but the air is still sufficiently rare to keep the probability of recombination at a low figure. Nearer still to the earth the number of free electrons produced per cubic metre falls, because the intensity of the ultraviolet radiation has been greatly reduced during its passage through the upper atmosphere. Also, since the atmosphere is relatively dense the probability of recombination is fairly high. The density of free electrons is therefore small immediately above the surface of the earth, rises at higher altitudes and then falls again at still greater heights. The earth is thus surrounded by a wide belt of ionized gas, known as the *ionosphere.*

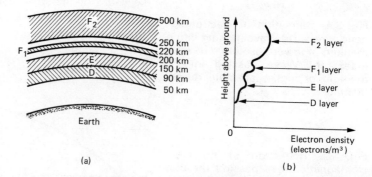

Fig. 3.6 Layers in the ionosphere

In the ionosphere, layers exist within which the free electron density is greater than at heights immediately above or below the layer. Four layers exist in the daytime: the D, E, F_1 and F_2 layers (Fig. 3.6).

At night-time the ultra-violet radiation ceases, no further free electrons are produced, and the D layer disappears because of the high rate of recombination at the lower altitudes. At 100 km or so above the earth, the recombination rate is much less and the E layer, although becoming weaker, does not normally disappear. During the hours of darkness the F_1 and F_2 layers merge to form a single F layer whose height varies considerably.

Refraction of the Sky Wave

Within an ionospheric layer the electron density *increases with increase in height* above the earth. It can be shown that the refractive index of a layer *decreases* with *increase* in electron density and with *decrease* in the frequency of the wave. Hence a wave of particular frequency is progressively refracted away from the normal as it travels upwards through a layer. If sufficient refraction occurs the wave will be returned to earth; if not, the wave will emerge from the top of the layer and travel upwards.

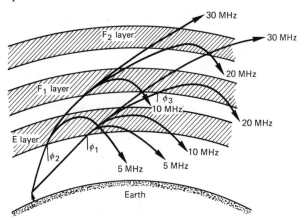

Fig. 3.7 Effect on ionospheric refraction of angle of incidence and the frequency of the wave

Suppose sky waves at frequencies 5, 10, 20 and 30 MHz are transmitted and are incident on the lower edge of the E layer with an angle of incidence ϕ_1 (Fig. 3.7). The 5 MHz wave is refracted to the greatest extent and is returned to earth after penetrating only a little way into the E layer. The 10 MHz wave must penetrate much farther into the E layer before it is returned to earth, while the 20 MHz wave is hardly refracted at all by the E layer and passes on to the F_1 layer. The 20 MHz wave meets the F_1 layer with a much larger angle of incidence, $\phi_3 > \phi_1$. A smaller change in direction is now required to return the wave to earth, and sufficient refraction is produced by the F_1 layer. The 30 MHz wave is not refracted to the extent required to return it to earth and escapes from the top of the F_2 layer.

If the angle at which the waves are incident on the E layer is reduced to ϕ_2, greater refraction is necessary to return the wave to earth. Consequently, only the 5 MHz wave is now returned by the E layer, the 10 MHz and 20 MHz waves passing right through and arriving at the F_1 layer. The refractive index of the F_1 layer is lower at 10 MHz than at 20 MHz; hence the 10 MHz wave is refracted sufficiently to be returned, but the 20 MHz wave is not. The 20 MHz wave passes on to the F_2 layer and is then returned. Once again the 30 MHz wave is not returned.

Further decrease in the angle of incidence of the waves on the E layer may result in the 20 MHz wave escaping the F_2

layer also and not returning to earth at all, the 5 MHz and 10 MHz waves being returned by a higher layer.

Sky-wave communication between two points up to about 2000 km apart is possible using the E layer, 3000 km using the F_1 layer, and about 4000 km using the F_2 layer. Communication over distances greater than 4000 km or so requires the use of two or more HOPS.

Critical Frequency at Vertical Incidence

If the angle of incidence made by the sky wave on the lower edge of the E layer is reduced to zero, the wave is then radiated vertically upwards from the transmitter. The maximum frequency that can thus be radiated and returned to earth by a layer is known as the *critical frequency at vertical incidence* of that layer. This frequency is of importance because (*a*) it can be measured and (*b*) it bears a simple relationship to the *maximum usable frequency* of a radio link.

Maximum Usable Frequency

The MAXIMUM USABLE FREQUENCY (m.u.f.) is the highest frequency that can be used to establish communication, using the sky wave, between two points. If a higher frequency is employed, the signal is not received at the distant end of the link.

As a wave travels through the ionosphere it is attenuated, the attenuation being inversely proportional to the frequency of the wave. It is therefore desirable to use as high a frequency as possible for communication over a radio link. The ionosphere does not, however, have constant characteristics and is subject to many fluctuations, and if the m.u.f. is employed for a link the signal may often not be received. Usually a frequency approximately 80–85% of the m.u.f. is used; this is known as the *optimum working (or traffic) frequency*. The m.u.f. of a link is not constant but varies with both time of day (being lower at night-time than in the daytime) and time of year (being lower in the winter than in the summer). To maintain reliable communication over a given link it is necessary to have a number of frequencies available so that the highest possible frequency can be used at all times. Sometimes it may be necessary to transmit simultaneously on more than one frequency, and if conditions are particularly poor to re-transmit when conditions improve.

Skip Distance

There is a minimum distance over which communication at a given frequency can be established by means of the sky wave.

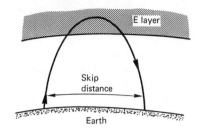

Fig. 3.8 Skip distance

Usually, the frequency considered is the m.u.f. of the link. If an attempt is made to reduce this minimum distance by using a smaller angle of incidence, the wave will not be returned to earth by the E layer but will pass through it. This minimum distance is known as the SKIP DISTANCE and is shown in Fig. 3.8. For a given frequency each of the ionospheric layers has its particular skip distance. It should be evident from the previous discussion that the higher the frequency of the wave the greater the skip distance.

Multiple-hop Transmissions

When communication is desired between two points which are more than about 4000 km apart it is necessary to employ two or more hops, as shown in Fig. 3.9. The sky wave is *refracted* in the ionosphere and returned to earth, and the downward wave is *reflected* at the surface of the earth to be returned skywards. The overall m.u.f. of a multi-hop link is the lowest of the m.u.f.s of the individual links.

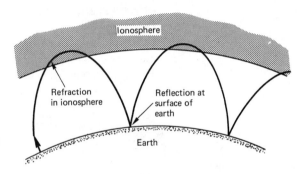

Fig. 3.9 Multi-hop transmission of sky wave

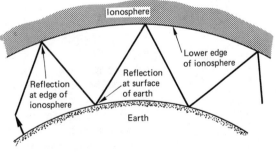

Fig. 3.10 Multi-hop transmission of low frequency wave

At very low and low frequencies the ionosphere acts as though it were an almost perfectly conducting surface and so v.l.f. and l.f. signals are *reflected* from the lower edge of the ionosphere. Worldwide, reliable communication is possible by multiple reflections between the ionosphere and the earth (Fig. 3.10).

The Space Wave

In the v.h.f. band aerials can be mounted several wavelengths above the surface of the earth. Communication is then by means of the *space wave*, which has two components, one direct and the other reflected from the earth as shown in Fig. 3.11*a*. The total field strength at the receiving aerial is the

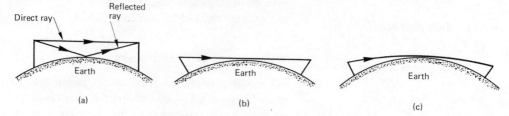

Fig. 3.11 Space wave propagation

phasor sum of the field strengths produced by energy arriving over each of the two paths. It would appear that the maximum possible spacing between the two aerials occurs when the direct wave just grazes the earth's surface at the centre of the link (Fig. 3.11*b*). Slight refraction of the direct wave occurs, however, and bends the wave around the surface of the earth. As a result the maximum possible range, illustrated in Fig. 13.11*c*, is somewhat greater than "line of sight."

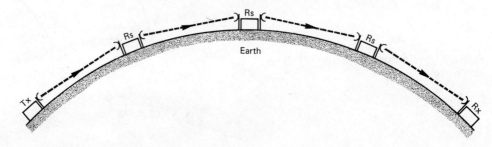

Fig. 3.12 Use of radio relay stations (Tx transmitter, Rx receiver, Rs relay station)

In practice, the average link length is shorter than the line-of-sight path length because this gives a considerable increase in the reliability of a link. For communication over longer distances it is necessary to employ a number of RELAY STATIONS. The principle of a long-distance v.h.f. or u.h.f. point-to-point system is shown by Fig. 3.12. The signal is radiated by the aerial at the transmitter end of the system and is received at the first of a chain of radio-relay stations. Here the signal is first amplified and is then transmitted on towards the next relay station. At the second relay station the received signal is amplified before it is transmitted towards the third station, and so on for all the relay stations forming a part of the route.

The space wave is also used for communication between a central base station and a number of mobile stations. Well-known examples of such systems are the police and fire brigade communication networks.

Fading

Fading, or changes in the amplitude of a received signal, is of two main types: *general fading*, in which the whole signal fades to the same extent; and *selective fading*, in which some of the frequency components of a signal fade while at the same time others increase in amplitude.

General Fading

As it travels through the ionosphere, a radio wave is attenuated, but since the ionosphere is in a continual state of flux the attenuation is not constant, and the amplitude of the received signal varies. Under certain conditions a complete fade-out of signals may occur for up to two hours. With the exception of complete fade-outs, general fading can be combated by *automatic gain control* (a.g.c.) in the radio receiver.

Selective Fading

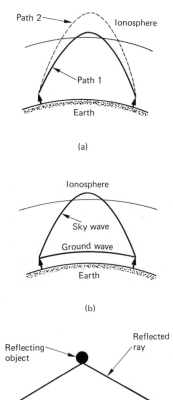

Fig. 3.13 Multi-path propagation

The radio waves arriving at the receiving end of a sky-wave radio link may have travelled over two or more different paths through the ionosphere (Fig. 3.13a). The total field strength at the receiving aerial is the phasor sum of the field strengths produced by each wave. Since the ionosphere is subject to continual fluctuations in its ionization density, the difference between the lengths of paths 1 and 2 will fluctuate and this will alter the total field strength at the receiver. Suppose, for example, that path 2 is initially one wavelength longer than path 1; the field strengths produced by the two waves are then in phase and the total field strength is equal to the algebraic sum of the individual field strengths.

If now a fluctuation occurs in the ionosphere causing the difference between the lengths of paths 1 and 2 to be reduced to a half-wavelength, the individual field strengths become in antiphase and the total field strength is given by their algebraic difference. The phase difference between the field strengths set up by the two waves is a function of frequency and hence the phasor sum of the two field strengths is different for each component frequency in the signal. This means that some frequencies may fade at the same instant as others are augmented; the effect is particularly serious in double-sideband amplitude-modulated systems because, if the carrier component fades to a level well below that of the two sidebands, the sidebands will beat together and considerable signal distortion will be produced.

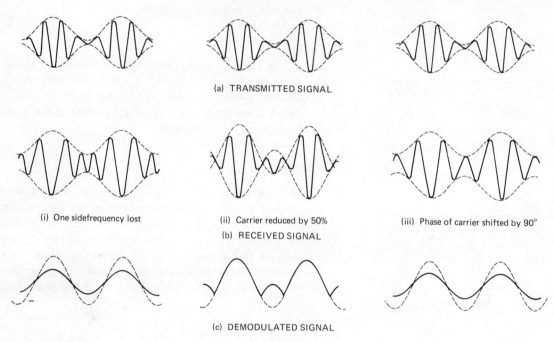

(a) TRANSMITTED SIGNAL

(i) One sidefrequency lost   (ii) Carrier reduced by 50%   (iii) Phase of carrier shifted by 90°

(b) RECEIVED SIGNAL

(c) DEMODULATED SIGNAL

Fig. 3.14 Selective fading

This effect is illustrated by the waveforms given in Fig. 3.14. Selective fading cannot be overcome by the use of a.g.c. in the receiver since this is operated by the carrier level only. Several methods of reducing selective fading do exist. For example, the use of frequencies as near to the m.u.f. as possible, the use of a transmitting aerial that radiates only one possible mode of propagation, the use of single-sideband or frequency-modulated systems, or the use of specialized equipment such as Lincompex.

Selective fading can also arise with systems using the surface (or ground) and space waves. In the daytime the D layer of the ionosphere completely absorbs any energy radiated skywards by a medium-wave broadcast aerial. At night the D layer disappears and any skywards radiation is returned to earth and will interfere with the surface wave, as shown in Fig. 3.13b. In the regions where the ground and sky waves are present at night, rapid fading, caused by fluctuations in the length of the sky path, occurs. This is why reception of medium-waveband broadcasts is much worse at night than in the daytime; it is minimized by the use of transmitting aerials having maximum gain along the surface of the earth and radiating minimum energy skywards.

Fig. 3.13c illustrates how multi-path reception of a v.h.f. signal can occur. Energy arrives at the receiver by a direct path and by reflection from a large object such as a hill or gasholder. If the reflecting object is not stationary, the phase difference between the two signals will change rapidly and rapid fading will occur. This is often observed on the screen of a television receiver when an aircraft is flying in the vicinity.

Use of Different Frequency Bands

By careful choice of operating frequency, communication can be maintained over most distances. Long-distance (thousands of kilometres), very reliable links can be set up using the ground wave in the very-low and low frequency bands. Since aerials are very inefficient at these frequencies, high power transmitters are necessary. This method of propagation is used for communication with ships at sea, for radio-navigation systems, for standard frequency transmissions, for some fixed point-to-point links, and for long-wave sound broadcasts.

In the MEDIUM-FREQUENCY BAND, the range of the ground wave is much smaller because of increasing ground losses. Reliable communication is possible over distances of up to some 80 to 320 km, depending on the transmitted power and the frequency. The sky wave is not available in the daytime, because of absorption in the D layer of the ionosphere, but at night-time it has a range of up to about 4000 km. A consequence of this is that medium wave sound broadcast signals are often subjected to considerable interference at night-time. Services provided in the medium frequency band, in addition to sound broadcasting, are radio-navigation, communications with aircraft and with ships at sea, and some fixed point-to-point services.

The range of the ground wave is severely limited at frequencies in the HIGH-FREQUENCY BAND and communication is generally established between two points using the sky wave. The maximum range possible using a single hop is about 4000 km but the use of several hops can extend this to about 16 000 km. A wide variety of different radio services are provided in the h.f. band; amongst these are sound broadcasting, communication with aircraft and with ships at sea, and international telephony circuits.

Above about 30 MHz, in the VERY HIGH FREQUENCY and ULTRA-HIGH FREQUENCY bands, communication between two points is only possible using the space wave† since the sky wave is not returned to earth at these frequencies. The maximum distance over which a link can be set up is restricted to the line-of-sight distance which, depending on the aerial heights, is generally some 40 to 60 km. When a longer-distance link is to be installed it is necessary to employ a number of relay stations. The v.h.f. and u.h.f. bands are also used for land mobile systems, such as police and fire radio communications, for point-to-point radio-telephony systems (generally multi-channel), for television broadcasting, for sound broadcasting, and for ship and air communications.

† Another type of propagation, *known as scatter*, is also available at certain frequencies in the v.h.f. and u.h.f. bands.

Exercises

3.1. Briefly explain the following terms in connection with radio wave propagation: (*a*) ionosphere, (*b*) skip distance, (*c*) sky wave, and (*d*) fading. (*C & G*)

3.2. Explain briefly how radio-wave propagation affects the practical application of transmission in the following frequency bands: (*a*) very low frequencies, say below 100 kHz, (*b*) high frequencies, say between 10 and 30 MHz, and (*c*) very high frequencies, say between 100 and 300 MHz. (*C & G*)

3.3. With the aid of simple sketches, explain the following terms in connection with radio-wave propagation: (*a*) ground waves, (*b*) sky waves, (*c*) critical frequency of an ionospheric layer, (*d*) skip distance, (*e*) maximum usable frequency. (*C & G*)

3.4. Explain briefly, with the aid of sketches, how multipath interference occurs in the following types of radio transmission: (*a*) medium-frequency broadcasting, (*b*) high-frequency long-distance telephony, (*c*) very-high frequency television broadcasting.

In each case state the methods which are adopted to reduce the effects of each form of interference. (*C & G*)

3.5. (*a*) At frequencies below 300 MHz there are two main phenomena which make world-wide communication possible. Describe these phenomena, stating their essential differences and the frequencies over which they function.

(*b*) In the high-frequency transmission over long distances, what factors govern the choice of frequencies for the most reliable point-to-point communications? (*C & G*)

3.6. Define the terms *critical frequency* and *maximum usable frequency* (m.u.f.) used in high-frequency propagation via the ionosphere. State the essential difference between these terms, and the normal range of frequencies involved. How will propagation characteristics vary with frequency about the m.u.f., and what would you recommend as an optimum frequency of operation in relation to the m.u.f.? (*C & G*)

3.7. (a) Describe two methods of obtaining long-distance radio communication at frequencies below 300 MHz. (b) Tabulate the essential differences between the two methods described in terms of carrier frequency, type of propagation, the service provided, and the transmitter power requirements. (C & G)

3.8. (a) Explain two methods of obtaining communication by radio beyond the horizon at frequencies below 300 MHz. (b) Describe the propagation characteristics of transmissions in the following frequency ranges; (i) very-low frequency, (ii) medium frequency, (iii) high frequency, (iv) very high frequency. (C&G)

3.9. (a) Describe briefly the effects of the ionosphere on radio communication over long distances. (b) State suitable frequencies below 300 MHz for transmissions providing the following types of services: (i) broadcasting over an area of radius about 40 km, (ii) point-to-point communication over distances in excess of 5000 km. (c) Explain the mode of propagation in each case. (C & G)

3.10. Explain, with the aid of sketches, five of the following terms used in long-distance radio communication: (i) ground wave, (ii) sky wave, (iii) ionosphere, (iv) space wave, (v) critical frequency at vertical incidence. (vi) maximum usable frequency. (C & G)

Short Exercises

3.11. What is meant by the polarization of a radio wave? Why is vertical polarization used in conjunction with the ground wave?

3.12. Distinguish between the surface wave, the ground wave, and the sky wave.

3.13. Describe how a sky wave directed into an ionospheric layer may be refracted and returned to earth.

3.14. Explain why a radio-telephony transmitter operating in the h.f. band is allocated a number of frequencies for use on a given route.

3.15. Explain why selective fading of radio waves occurs.

3.16. Describe the use of the v.h.f. band for point-to-point communication.

3.17. Write notes to outline the way in which the ionosphere is formed.

3.18. Explain why the skip distance cannot be increased by increasing the transmitted power.

3.19. A sky wave h.f. radio link employs three hops. The maximum usable frequencies of the three hops are, respectively, 5.5 MHz, 6.5 MHz, and 6.1 MHz. What is the overall maximum usable frequency?

3.20. Explain why it may be easier to establish a low-frequency radio link using reflection from the lower edge of the D layer in a North-to-South direction than in an East-to-West-direction.

4 Radio Receiver Circuits

The principles of operation of radio receivers will be described in the Chapter 5. In this chapter the operation of the circuits commonly employed in modern radio receivers will be described.

Tuned Amplifiers

A TUNED AMPLIFIER is one which is required to handle a relatively narrow band of frequencies centred about a particular radio frequency. Such an amplifier has two main functions: firstly, to provide a specified gain over a given frequency band, and secondly, to provide the selectivity necessary to ensure that frequencies outside the wanted band are not amplified. A parallel-resonant circuit is used as the collector load, and this is tuned to the required operating frequency and designed to have the wanted 3 dB bandwidth. The required LC product is fairly small and is easily obtained; the capacitances inherent in the device and stray capacitances that adversely affect the performance of an untuned amplifier now contribute to the capacitance of the tuned circuit.

Transistors may be subject to considerable internal feedback at radio frequencies and a transistor tuned amplifier must be designed to prevent instability. Generally the *common-emitter* configuration is employed because it provides the greatest gain, it is less prone to instability, and its input and output impedances have more convenient values. The *common-base* connection is chosen when one or more of its particular characteristics are required. These are as follows: (a) it gives a more or less constant gain over a wide bandwidth, (b) the spread in the current gains of different transistors of the same type is smaller since $h_{fe} = h_{fb}/(1 - h_{fb})$; this ensures that replacing a transistor will not result in a much-changed amplifier performance, and (c) a transistor in common base can provide a higher gain at frequencies near the f_t of the transistor than the same transistor in common-emitter.† The choice of connection depends upon which will give the greater and more stable gain.

Manufacturing tolerances on the components used in an r.f. amplifier mean that at least one variable tuning component, such as an inductor or a capacitor, is required so that the circuit can be initially adjusted, or *aligned*. Some amplifiers, such as the *intermediate frequency* (i.f.) amplifiers in a superheterodyne radio receiver operate at a fixed frequency and, after alignment, are not normally readjusted. Other amplifiers are required to operate at different frequencies and must therefore be *tuned* to the required frequency.

A transistor amplifier stage takes an input current, and hence an input power, and is essentially a power amplifier; for maximum power gain, each stage must be matched, or nearly matched, to the following stage. The interstage coupling network must determine the centre frequency and bandwidth of the stage while, at the same time, transfering sufficient r.f. power to the next stage and also providing matching.

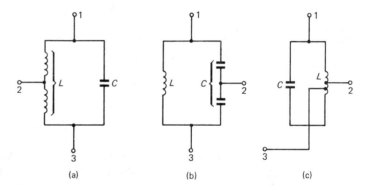

Fig. 4.1 Three methods of tapping a parallel-tuned circuit

The resonant frequency of a parallel-tuned circuit is not changed if the inductor is tapped (Fig. 4.1*a*) or the capacitance is split into two (Fig. 4.1*b*). The impedance seen looking into terminals 1 and 2 is much smaller than the impedance seen looking into terminals 1 and 3, the reduction depending upon the inductance (or capacitance) ratio. If terminals 1 and 3 are connected to the output terminals of one transistor, and terminals 1 and 2 are connected to the input terminals of the following transistor, suitable choice of the inductance (or capacitance) ratio can give the required impedance values. The voltage gain of a tuned amplifier is determined by both the

† f_t is the frequency at which the magnitude of the short-circuit current gain in common-emitter $|h_{fe}|$ has fallen to unity. It is also the product of $|h_{fe}|$ and the frequency of operation, i.e. if $f_t = 100$ MHz, $|h_{fe}| = 1$; at 50 MHz, $|h_{fe}| = 2$; at 10 MHz, $|h_{fe}| = 10$, and so on.

current gain of the transistor and the impedance of the collector tuned circuit. Thus the gain/frequency characteristic of a tuned amplifier is determined by the selectivity of its tuned collector load and a typical characteristic is shown in Fig. 4.2.

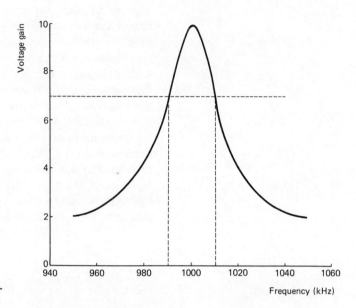

Fig. 4.2 Gain/frequency characteristic of a tuned amplifier

The BANDWIDTH of a tuned amplifier is normally taken as the width of the band of frequencies over which the gain is not more than 3 dB down ($1/\sqrt{2}$ times) on the gain at the resonant frequency. Thus, the bandwidth of the amplifier gain characteristic shown in Fig. 4.3 is 20 kHz. The output impedance of the transistor and, more particularly, the input impedance of the transistor used in the following stage will appear in parallel with the dynamic resistance of the tuned circuit. If a narrow bandwidth is required (good selectivity), the dynamic resistance R_d of the tuned circuit must not be much reduced by the parallel resistances.

The input resistance of a common-emitter connected transistor is fairly low, generally in the range 500–2000 Ω, and so must not be connected across the complete tuned circuit. Otherwise R_d would be reduced to a small value and both the gain and the selectivity of the amplifier would suffer. The output impedance of a transistor is considerably larger, usually at least 20 kΩ, and it is possible to connect its collector-base terminals directly across the tuned circuit without excessive damping taking place. Sometimes, however, to minimize the loading on the tuned circuit and to achieve maximum selectivity, the collector is also connected to a tap (see Fig. 4.1*c*).

Fig. 4.3 shows the circuits of two TUNED-COLLECTOR TRANSISTOR AMPLIFIERS. The tuned circuit is formed by L in parallel with the capacitors C_2 and C_3 in Fig. 4.3a and C_2 alone in Fig. 4.3b, plus the transistor and stray capacitances.

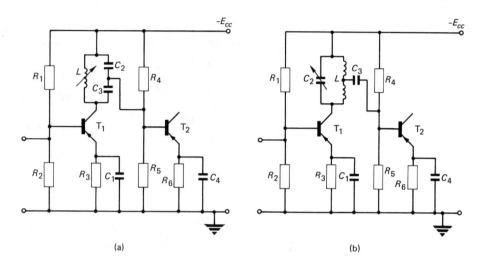

(a)   (b)

Fig. 4.3 Tuned-collector transistor amplifiers

At higher frequencies the transistor and stray capacitances may be sufficiently large for a physical tuning capacitor to be unnecessary. Figs. 4.3a and b are completed by the resistors R_1 to R_6 and their associated decoupling capacitors; these provide bias and d.c. stabilization for the circuits. The only component not mentioned is capacitor C_3 in Fig. 4.3b; this blocks d.c. and prevents the bias arrangement for transistor T_2 being upset.

The tuned-collector load has its maximum impedance of $R_d = L/Cr$ ohms at the resonant frequency of $f_0 = 1/2\pi\sqrt{(LC)}$ Hz. Here r is the resistance of the inductor winding and C is the resultant capacitance of the collector circuit, consisting of the parallel combination of the total circuit capacitance, the capacitances of T_1 and T_2, and the various stray capacitances. The magnitude of R_d is reduced to a lower figure by the shunting effects of the output resistance of T_1 and the input resistance of T_2, modified by the tuned circuit tapping ratios.

An alternative method of coupling r.f. tuned amplifier stages is the use of INDUCTIVE COUPLING with either the primary or the secondary winding tuned, by means of a variable capacitor, to resonance at the desired operating frequency.

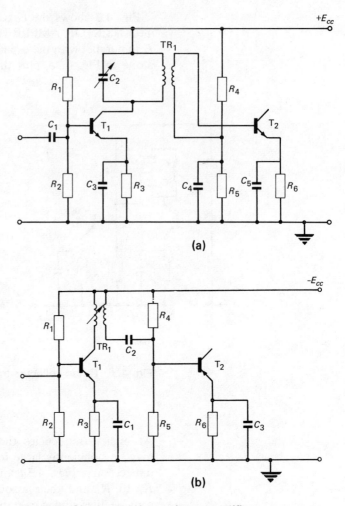

Fig. 4.4 Single-tuned transistor amplifiers

Generally, because of the low input resistance of a transistor, it is the primary circuit that is tuned. The circuit of a SINGLE-TUNED transistor amplifier is given in Fig. 4.4. R_1 to R_6 are conventional d.c. bias and stability components and C_3, C_4 and C_5 are decoupling components. The primary winding of r.f. transformer TR_1 is tuned to resonate at the signal frequency by variable capacitor C_2. The secondary winding of TR_1 has fewer turns than the primary winding so that the low input resistance of T_2 will be stepped up to the correct collector load resistance for T_1.

Another version of the single-tuned transistor amplifier is shown in Fig. 4.4b. The primary winding of transformer TR_1 is in parallel with the various stray capacitances in the collector circuit and a physical tuning capacitor is not used. Tuning to the required frequency is effected by the movement of a screw-in ferrite core altering the inductance of the winding. Capacitor C_2 is provided to block the collector supply and ensure that the bias for T_2 is provided solely by the bias circuit. The remainder of the components have conventional bias and d.c. stabilization functions.

Very often the gain required from an amplifier is greater than can be obtained from a single stage, and then two or more stages may be coupled IN CASCADE to produce the required gain. The overall gain A of a multi-stage amplifier is the product of the individual stage gains. For example, if the three stages of an amplifier have voltage gains of 10, 12, and 8 respectively, the overall gain of the circuit is 960. If four identical stages, each having a gain of 10, are cascaded the overall gain is 10^4.

Cascading stages also has the effect of reducing the 3 dB bandwidth of the amplifier. Consider, for example, the four identical stages previously mentioned. Suppose the lower and upper 3 dB frequencies of each stage are f_1 and f_2 respectively; then the gain per stage at these frequencies is $10/\sqrt{2}$. The overall gain at frequencies f_1 and f_2 is therefore $(10/\sqrt{2})^4$, or 1250, and this is much less than 3 dB down on 10^4. The overall 3 dB bandwidth, i.e. the frequency band between the "gain $= 10^4/\sqrt{2}$ points," is obviously smaller than $f_2 - f_1$. *Bandwidth shrinkage* is illustrated by Fig. 4.5.

The gain/frequency characteristics of the single-tuned amplifiers mentioned so far are rounded and fall away on either side of resonance. As a result a single-tuned amplifier cannot discriminate against unwanted frequencies near resonance without at the same time discriminating against some of the wanted frequencies. This disadvantage can be overcome in tuned amplifiers designed to work at a constant frequency, such as intermediate-frequency amplifiers in superheterodyne receivers, by the use of double-tuned transformer coupling.

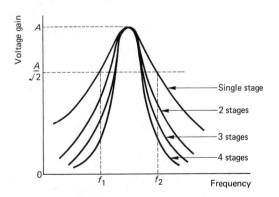

Fig. 4.5 Bandwidth shrinkage

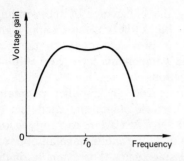

Fig. 4.6 Gain/frequency characteristic of a double-tuned amplifier

A DOUBLE-TUNED AMPLIFIER employs transformer coupling in which both primary and secondary circuits are tuned to resonate at the desired operating frequency. If the coupling between the windings is critical, a more or less flat-topped characteristic is obtained and the circuit will discriminate sharply against unwanted frequencies lying outside the flat top (Fig. 4.6). The use of double-tuned amplifiers is generally restricted to fixed-frequency applications, because of difficulties associated with the need for the simultaneous tuning of two coupled tuned circuits.

The circuit of a double-tuned transistor amplifier is shown in Fig. 4.7. Both the primary and the secondary windings of transformer TR_1 are tuned to the required centre frequency and the coupling between the windings is adjusted until a flat-topped response is obtained. When the inductance of the secondary winding is large, the connection to the base of the following transistor is made via a tap as shown, but if the secondary inductance is small the tap is not necessary.

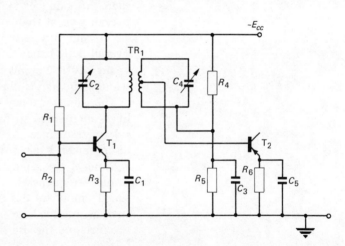

Fig. 4.7 The double-tuned transistor amplifier

Because of the relatively low input resistance of transistor T_2 the loading on the secondary tuned circuit can be large, and double-tuning may offer little, if any, improvement in performance. For this reason, many i.f. amplifiers in transistor radio receivers employ single-tuned circuits.

Detectors

In a radio receiver the intelligence signal must be extracted from the modulated wave appearing at the output of the final i.f. amplifier before use can be made of it, because if the modulated wave were applied directly to a loudspeaker or telephone receiver the instrument would not be able to respond. Even if it could, the resulting sounds would be above the range of frequencies the human ear is capable of hearing. The extraction of the intelligence signal from a modulated wave is known as detection or demodulation, and the circuit employed is known as a DETECTOR or demodulator. Generally, the terms demodulation and demodulator are restricted to applications of s.s.b. amplitude-modulated signals. In this chapter only the detection of d.s.b. amplitude-modulated waves is to be discussed.

With amplitude modulation the intelligence signal is carried in the form of variations in the amplitude of a carrier wave, and the process of detection involves the production of a voltage that varies in the same way as the envelope of the modulated carrier wave. The output signal of an ideal detector is an exact replica of the intelligence signal modulated on to the carrier applied to the detector. If the output signal is not identical with the intelligence signal, some distortion has been introduced by the detector.

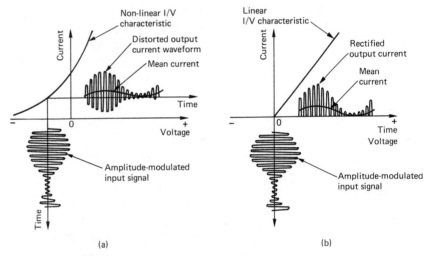

Fig. 4.8 Principle of (*a*) a non-linear detector and (*b*) a linear detector

A number of different kinds of detector circuit exist but most of them can be placed into one of two categories: (*a*) non-linear detectors and (*b*) linear detectors. A NON-LINEAR detector is a detector that has a non-linear current/voltage characteristic, as in Fig. 4.8*a*, and that detects by distorting the input waveform and extracting the mean value of the resulting output current. A LINEAR detector, on the other hand, has a linear current/voltage characteristic (Fig. 4.8*b*) and performs the operation of detection by rectifying the input waveform and extracting the mean value of the resulting output current. In both cases the mean value, or d.c. component, fluctuates at the frequency of the modulating intelligence signal. Distortion, or rectification, of the input waveform, before the mean value of the output current is extracted, is necessary because the mean value of an undistorted amplitude-modulated wave over a large number of carrier cycles is zero.

A non-linear detector is the more sensitive because the required output voltage is proportional to the square of the input carrier voltage, whereas the output voltage of a linear detector is only proportional to the input carrier voltage itself.

The Diode Detector

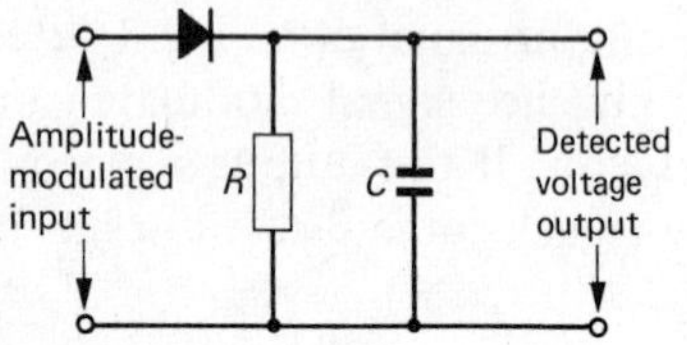

The diode detector is the most commonly used type of detector because it is capable of detection with the least distortion and it is also the cheapest circuit. Fig. 4.9 shows the circuit of a DIODE DETECTOR that consists essentially of a diode connected in series with a parallel resistor-capacitor network.

Consider an amplitude-modulated wave to be applied to the input terminals of the circuit shown in Fig. 4.9 and suppose the capacitor to be disconnected. The diode will conduct during those half-cycles of the input signal that make its p-type region positive with respect to its n-type region. Current will flow in a series of pulses whose amplitude is proportional to the amplitude of the voltage applied to the diode. The current pulses flow in the diode load resistor R and develop a voltage across it that varies in the manner shown in Fig. 4.8b. The mean value of the load voltage varies at the wanted modulation frequency and so detection has taken place. This simple circuit is an inefficient detector because only $1/\pi$ times the input voltage is available at the output terminals as the detected output.

A number of other components, at d.c., at the carrier frequency, and at harmonics of the carrier frequency, are also present.

If the capacitor is re-connected in the position shown in Fig. 4.9, the detection efficiency η (η is defined as the ratio of peak output voltage at modulating frequency to peak input voltage), is improved approximately π times. The action of the capacitor in effecting this improvement is as follows. If an unmodulated carrier wave of constant amplitude is applied to the detector, the first positive half-cycle of the wave will cause the diode to conduct. The diode current will charge the capacitor to a voltage that is slightly less than the peak value of the input signal (slightly less because of a small voltage drop in the diode itself). At the end of this first half-cycle, the diode ceases to conduct and the capacitor starts to discharge through

Amplitude-modulated input R C Detected voltage output

Fig. 4.9 Diode detector circuit

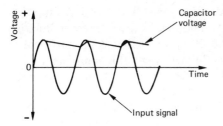

Fig. 4.10 Output voltage of a diode detector handling a signal of constant amplitude

the load resistor R at a rate determined by the TIME CONSTANT, CR seconds, of the discharge circuit. The time constant is chosen to ensure that the capacitor has not discharged very much before the next positive half-cycle of the input signal arrives to recharge the capacitor (see Fig. 4.10). The time constant for the charging of the capacitor is equal to Cr seconds, where r is the forward resistance of the diode and is much less than R. A nearly constant d.c. voltage is developed across the load resistor R; the fluctuations that exist are small and take place at the frequency of the input carrier signal.

If, now, the input signal is amplitude-modulated, the voltage across the diode load will vary in sympathy with the wave envelope, provided the time constant is small enough. The capacitor must be able to discharge rapidly enough for the voltage across it to follow those parts of the modulation cycle when the modulation envelope is decreasing in amplitude (see Fig. 4.11). The capacitor voltage falls until a positive half-cycle of the input signal makes the diode conduct and recharge the capacitor. When the modulation envelope is decreasing, one positive half-cycle is of lower peak value than the preceding positive half-cycle, and the capacitor is recharged to a smaller voltage.

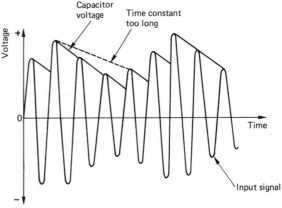

Fig. 4.11 Output voltage of a diode detector handling an amplitude-modulated signal

If the time constant of the discharge path is too long, relative to the periodic time of the modulating signal, the capacitor voltage will not be able to follow the troughs of the modulation envelope; that is, the decay curve passes right over the top of one or more input voltage peaks, as shown by the dotted line in Fig. 4.11, and waveform distortion takes place. The time constant must not be too short, however, or the voltage across the load resistor will not be as large as it could be, because insufficient charge will be stored between successive pulses of diode current. The time constant determines the rapidity with which the detected voltage can change, and must be long compared with the periodic time of the carrier wave and short compared with the periodic time of the modulating signal.

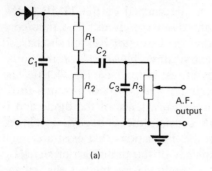

(a)

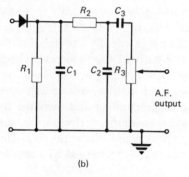

(b)

Fig. 4.12 Diode detector filter circuits

The voltage developed across the diode load resistor has three components: (a) a component at the wanted modulating signal frequency, (b) a d.c. component that is proportional to the peak value of the unmodulated wave (this component is not wanted for detection and must be prevented from reaching the following audio-frequency amplifier stage) and (c) components at the carrier frequency and harmonics of the carrier frequency that must also be prevented from reaching the audio-frequency amplifier. To eliminate the unwanted components the detector output is fed into a resistance-capacitance filter network before application to the audio-frequency amplifier.

The d.c. component is removed by a series capacitor and the r.f. components are removed by a suitable RC filter. Two possible arrangements are shown in Fig. 4.12. At (a) capacitor C_2 is the d.c. blocker and $C_3 R_3$ is the r.f. filter; R_3 also functions as a volume control. At (b), R_2 and C_2 remove the r.f. components, and the d.c. component is removed by capacitor C_3; R_3 is again the volume control.

The Transistor Detector

The circuit of a common-emitter transistor detector is shown in Fig. 4.13. Rectification takes place in the emitter/base circuit and the rectified signal is amplified by the transistor in the usual way.

Components R_1, R_2, R_4, C_2 and C_3 provide bias and d.c. stabilization and R_3 is the collector load resistor. C_4 is a by-pass capacitor which prevents voltages at the carrier frequency appearing across R_3 and being fed, via C_5, to the output terminals of the circuit. The input amplitude-modulated signal is fed into the base/emitter circuit via r.f. transformer TR_1, the primary winding of which is tuned to the carrier frequency. The base/emitter junction of transistor T_1 acts as a semiconductor diode and together with R_2 and C_2 forms a diode detector. The detected voltage appears across R_2 and varies the emitter/base bias voltage of the transistor

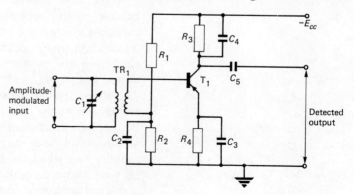

Fig. 4.13 The transistor detector

and this variation causes the collector current to vary in accordance with the modulation envelope. A voltage at the modulating signal frequency appears across the collector load resistor R_3, and this is coupled to the load by capacitor C_5.

A detector circuit using a transistor connected in the common-base configuration is also possible, detection again taking place in the emitter/base circuit.

Many communication receivers operate with single sideband a.m. signals. Since such signals do not include a carrier component, a diode detector cannot be used and often a balanced modulator is employed as a demodulator.

Audio Amplifiers

The purpose of the audio amplifier stage in a radio receiver is to amplify the modulation signal output of the detector stage to the level required to operate the loudspeaker, or telephone instrument, associated with the receiver. Alternatively, the audio amplifier may be required to supply power to a transmission line linking the receiver to some distant point. For example, a particular communication receiver might have the capability to supply 1.0 W to a loudspeaker, or 2 mW to a telephone instrument, or 25 mW to a 600 Ω transmission line.

Often the audio amplifier consists of a *pre-amplifier* stage [see EII] which amplifies the voltage output of the detector to the level required to drive the POWER AMPLIFIER output stage.

A power amplifier is one in which the output power is the main consideration. If an appreciable power output is required, a large input signal is necessary in order to obtain large swings of output current and output voltage. This is the purpose of the pre-amplifier or *driver* stage. The transistor used in a power amplifier must be chosen so that its maximum current, voltage and power ratings are not exceeded. These figures are supplied by the manufacturer.

For the maximum power to be delivered by a power amplifier to its load, without exceeding a predetermined distortion level, the transistor should work into a particular load impedance, known as the *optimum load*. Rarely will the actual load be equal to this optimum value and so transformer coupling is normally used, Fig. 4.14. Transformer coupling also reduces the d.c. power lost in the circuit because the transformer primary winding usually has a low d.c. resistance.

The turns ratio $n(=N_1/N_2)$ of the output transformer is chosen to transform the actual load R_L into the optimum load R_L' of the transistor or valve, i.e.

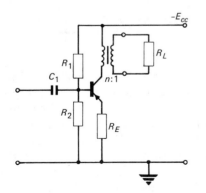

Fig. 4.14 Transistor transformer-coupled power amplifier

$$n = \sqrt{\frac{R_L'}{R_L}} \tag{4.1}$$

EXAMPLE 4.1

The optimum load for a particular output transistor is $490\,\Omega$. What turns ratio is required in the output transformer to match the transistor to a $4\,\Omega$ moving-coil loudspeaker?

Solution

$$n = \sqrt{\frac{490}{4}} = 11.06 \qquad (Ans.)$$

D.C. stabilization of a transistor amplifier is best achieved using the potential-divider bias circuit, but to minimize d.c. power losses, the emitter resistance should be of low value, perhaps as small as $1\,\Omega$. When such a low value of emitter resistance is used, the resistor is not decoupled because the required capacitance would be extremely high. In amplifiers with a power output of several watts and a collector current of several amperes, the emitter resistor may sometimes be omitted.

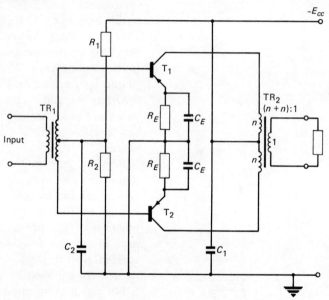

Fig. 4.15 Class A push-pull amplifier

When the output power available from a given transistor used in a single-ended circuit is inadequate, the *push-pull* connection, shown in Fig. 4.15, is often used. The input and output transformers, TR_1 and TR_2 are accurately centre-tapped, and Class A bias is provided by R_1, R_2 and R_E. Separate emitter resistors have been shown in Fig. 4.15 and have the advantage of permitting an accurate d.c. balance to be obtained between the two halves of the circuit. Alternatively, a common emitter resistor may be used; if this resistor is not decoupled the a.c. balance of the circuit is improved.

In the absence of an input signal a steady collector current flows in each half of the circuit, and the two currents flow in opposite directions in the two halves of the output transformer primary winding (Fig. 4.16*a*) tending to produce equal m.m.f.s of opposite polarity, so that d.c. saturation of the core is avoided. These m.m.f.s are completely cancelled if the two halves of the circuit are balanced. Saturation of the core would cause waveform distortion. A physically smaller core, perhaps without an air gap, may be employed, and this means that the output transformer can be both smaller and lighter than the output transformer required for a single-ended stage producing the same power output.

When a signal is applied to the input terminals of a PUSH-PULL AMPLIFIER, the two transistors are driven in antiphase. Referring to Fig. 4.16*b*, during the half-cycle of the input signal which makes point A positive with respect to point B, the e.m.f. induced in the secondary winding of the input

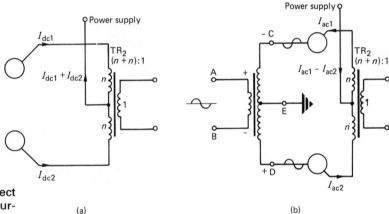

Fig. 4.16 Showing (*a*) the direct currents and (*b*) the alternating currents flowing in a push-pull circuit

(a)   (b)

transformer TR_1 makes point C negative relative to point D. Point C is then negative and point D positive with respect to earth. The a.c. components of the two collector currents are then in antiphase with one another. The two signal currents flow in the same direction in the output transformer primary winding and hence the a.c. flux set up in the core is proportional to the *sum* of the two currents. The a.c. flux in the core cuts the turns of the secondary winding where it induces an alternating e.m.f., so that, if the secondary winding is closed in a load impedance, a load current flows.

All second and higher-order even-harmonic components generated by the transistors are reduced to a very low level. This means that an output power of more than twice that available from one transistor can be obtained for the same distortion. Alternatively, the same power output with smaller distortion can be obtained.

Many push-pull amplifiers are operated under Class B conditions, i.e. with the transistors biased nearly to cut-off. One possible circuit arrangement is the same as that shown in Fig. 4.15. When a sinusoidal input signal is applied to the circuit, one transistor conducts during positive half-cycles and the other conducts on negative half-cycles. The collector current of each transistor flows in a series of half-sinewave pulses, and the two currents combine in the output transformer to produce a sinusoidal output waveform. Class B operation has the advantages over Class A of higher efficiency and much smaller current taken from the supply under quiescent conditions. The main disadvantage is that distortion of the output waveform is greater, very largely because of crossover distortion.

The mutual characteristics (I_c/V_{be}) of a transistor are not linear at low current values and this gives rise to the collector current waveform shown in Fig. 4.17. In order to minimize crossover distortion, both the transistors must be biased to conduct a small quiescent current. The price to be paid for this is a reduction in the efficiency of the amplifier.

The need for relatively expensive and bulky centre-tapped input and output transformers can be avoided by the use of the COMPLEMENTARY SYMMETRY Class B circuit shown in Fig. 4.18. T_1 is the driver transistor while T_2 and T_3 form a Class B push-pull output stage; notice that T_2 is a n-p-n and T_3 is a p-n-p transistor. The bias voltage for the driver stage transistor is derived from the junction of the output emitter resistors R_6 and R_7, while the bias for the output transistors is obtained from the collector circuit of T_1. In the absence of an input signal, the d.c. conditions of the circuit are such that a small current is conducted by both transistors, and the potential at the junction of R_6 and R_7 is approximately equal to one half the supply voltage $E_{cc}/2$. The voltage at the junction of R_4 and R_5 is then slightly more positive than $E_{cc}/2$. The collector potential of T_1 is slightly less positive than $E_{cc}/2$. The resistance values of R_4 and R_5 cannot be high since they must pass the quiescent collector current of T_1, and this must be greater than the peak value of the base current required to drive an output transistor into the saturated condition.

When a sinusoidal input signal is applied to T_1, an alternating voltage is developed across its collector load $R_4 + R_5$. During the positive half cycles of the input signal voltage, the collector potential of T_1 becomes less positive and T_3 conducts more current, reaching saturation at the peak of the input half cycle. At the same time the point marked X also becomes less positive and T_2 is turned off. Similarly, during the negative half cycles of the input signal the base potentials of T_2 and T_3 are taken more positive with respect to their emitter potentials, and this results in T_2 conducting and T_3 switching off. The

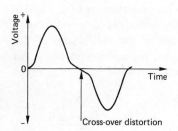

Fig. 4.17 Cross-over distortion

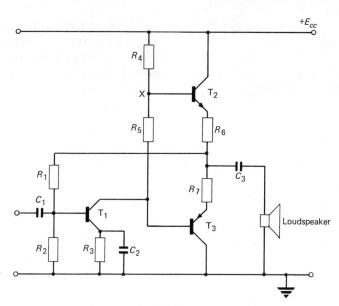

Fig. 4.18 Complementary symmetry Class B push-pull amplifier

output transistors take it in turn to supply current to the loudspeaker. The voltage developed across the loudspeaker varies sinusoidally with a peak value of very nearly $E_{cc}/2$ volts.

Oscillators

An oscillator is an electronic circuit designed to produce an alternating e.m.f. of known frequency and waveform. In this chapter only oscillator circuits which produce an output voltage of sinusoidal waveform will be discussed.

When an oscillator is first switched on, a current surge in the frequency-determining network produces a voltage, at the required frequency of oscillation, across the network. A fraction of this voltage is fed back to the input terminals of the amplifier and is amplified to reappear across the network. A fraction of this larger voltage is then also fed back to the input and further amplified, and so on. In this way the amplitude of the signal voltage builds up until the gain is reduced in some way to make the loop gain unity. The gain may be reduced either by the transistor driving into saturation or by operating the circuit under Class C conditions.

The frequency-determining section of an oscillator may consist of an LC tuned circuit, a resistance-capacitance network, a piezoelectric crystal or, at higher frequencies, a length of short-circuited transmission line. In this chapter, however, only LC and crystal oscillators will be discussed.

The important characteristics of an oscillator are its frequency or frequencies (if variable) of operation, its frequency stability, and its amplitude stability. The STABILITY of an

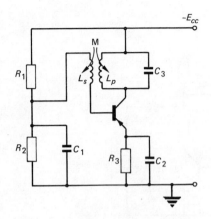

Fig. 4.19 Tuned-collector oscillator

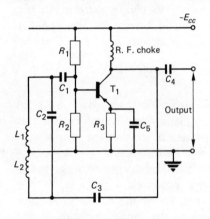

Fig. 4.20 The Hartley oscillator

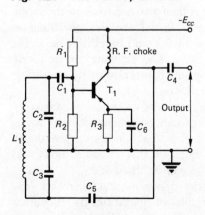

Fig. 4.21 The Colpitts oscillator

oscillator is the degree to which the output frequency or amplitude remains constant over a predetermined period. With a laboratory oscillator other obvious factors of interest are the cost, size and weight of the instrument and its expected reliability in the anticipated conditions of use.

LC Oscillators

An *LC* oscillator must contain a frequency-determining section and a maintaining section; the former is provided by a parallel-resonant circuit and the latter by a transistor amplifier. The bias and d.c. stabilization requirements of a transistor oscillator are similar to those of a transistor amplifier and the same circuitry is used. The circuit of a tuned-collector oscillator is given in Fig. 4.19. The frequency-determining parallel-resonant circuit is connected in the collector circuit of the transistor.

The operation of this circuit is as follows. When the supply voltage is switched on, any noise or small voltage fluctuation in the input circuit is amplified and appears at the collector. The parallel-resonant circuit is tuned to the required frequency, and only at this frequency does an appreciable oscillatory current flow. The current flowing in the primary winding L_p induces an e.m.f. at the same frequency into the secondary coil L_s and this voltage is applied to the input terminals of the valve (or transistor). The transistor introduces a phase shift of 180° and therefore the transformer must be arranged to give a further 180° shift to make the loop phase shift zero. The mutual inductance between the primary and secondary windings must be large enough to ensure a loop gain greater than unity. The frequency of oscillation is approximately equal to the resonant frequency of the parallel-resonant circuit, i.e.

$$f_{osc} \approx \frac{1}{2\pi\sqrt{(L_p C_3)}}$$

Fig. 4.20 shows a transistor HARTLEY OSCILLATOR. Capacitors C_3 and C_4 are d.c. blocks and have negligible reactance at the frequency of oscillation; conversely the r.f. choke has a very high reactance and prevents oscillation-frequency currents from entering the power supply.

The frequency-determining resonant circuit is formed by L_1 and L_2 in parallel with C_2 and the remainder of the components provide bias and d.c. stability. If the inductors L_1 and L_2 are replaced by a single inductor, and capacitor C_2 is split into two parts whose junction is earthed, a COLPITTS OSCILLATOR is obtained (Fig. 4.21).

The Colpitts circuit has the following advantages over the Hartley oscillator: (*a*) it does not require a tapped inductor, and (*b*) at higher frequencies it is both easier to adjust and less prone to oscillation at unwanted frequencies. However, in the majority of cases the circuit giving the most convenient values of inductance and capacitance would be chosen.

Frequency Stability

The frequency stability of an oscillator is the amount by which its frequency drifts from the designed value. In most cases it is desirable that the drift should be very small, and the maximum allowable change is generally specified as so many parts per million. The frequency of oscillation is also a function of both the load into which the oscillator works and the parameters of the transistor.

Load on the Oscillator

The frequency of oscillation is dependent on the magnitude of the load into which the oscillator delivers its output power. If the load is not constant in magnitude, the oscillation frequency will not be stable. Variations in the external load can be effectively removed by feeding it via a buffer amplifier, i.e. an amplifier circuit whose functions are to isolate the oscillator from any changes in the load and to increase the power output.

Variations in Supply Voltage

The parameters of a transistor, such as current gain and input and output capacitance, are functions of the quiescent or collector current and hence of the supply voltage. Any change in the supply voltage will cause one or more parameters to vary and the oscillation frequency to drift. This cause of frequency instability is usually fairly small but, if necessary, the stabilization of the power supply must be improved.

Tuned Circuit Components

Changes in the temperature of the tuned circuit components produce changes in the inductance and capacitance and hence in the frequency of oscillation. Temperature changes alter the inductance by changing the dimensions of the wire and of the former on which it is wound. The capacitance is a function of temperature because the capacitor plates expand or contract slightly, and also because the permittivity of the dielectric is not quite independent of temperature. The frequency stability can be improved by minimizing temperature changes by (*a*) using a low-power transistor, (*b*) keeping the tuned circuit well clear of any source of heat, and (*c*) (if the expense is justified) mounting the tuned circuit inside a thermostatically-controlled enclosure or *oven* that is kept a few degrees above the ambient temperature. Temperature changes can also be minimized by keeping the oscillator permanently switched on.

When all temperature changes have been minimized, a further improvement in frequency stability can be achieved by using components having small and/or opposite temperature coefficients. Silvered-mica capacitors are often used, because, typically, they have a temperature coefficient of about +20 parts per million per degree. However, if a mixture of ceramic and titanium is used as the dielectric a negative temperature coefficient of up to about 400 parts per million per degree is possible. The practical difficulty inherent in the use of a negative-temperature-coefficient capacitor is that the inductor and capacitor values must track one another and be economically reproducible in quantity production.

The best frequency stability that can be achieved with an *LC* oscillator is about 10 parts in 10^6 per degree and if better stability is required a *crystal* oscillator must be used. A piezoelectric crystal is a material, such as quartz, having the property that, if subjected to a mechanical stress, a potential difference is developed across it, and if the stress is reversed a p.d. of opposite polarity is developed. Conversely, the application of a potential difference to a piezoelectric crystal causes the crystal to be stressed in a direction depending on the polarity of the applied voltage.

In its natural state quartz crystal is of hexagonal cross-section with pointed ends. If a small, thin plate is cut from a crystal, the plate will have a particular natural frequency, and if an alternating voltage at its natural frequency is applied across it, the plate will vibrate vigorously. The natural frequency of a crystal plate depends upon its dimensions, the mode of vibration, and its original position or *cut* in the crystal. The important characteristics of a particular cut are its natural frequency and its temperature coefficient; one cut, the *GT cut*, has a negligible temperature coefficient over a temperature range from 0°C to 100°C; another cut, the *AT cut*, has a temperature coefficient that varies from about +10 p.p.m./°C at 0°C to 0 p.p.m./°C at 40°C and about +20 p.p.m./°C at 90°C. Crystal plates are available with fundamental natural frequencies from 4 kHz up to about 10 MHz or so. For higher frequencies the required plate thickness is very small and the plate is fragile; however, a crystal can be operated at a harmonic of its fundamental frequency and such *overtone* operation raises the possible upper frequency to about 100 MHz.

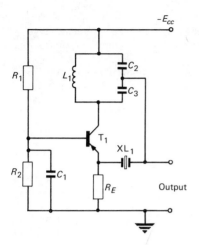

Fig. 4.22 Crystal oscillator

Fig. 4.22 shows the circuit of a transistor crystal oscillator that employs a crystal operating in its series-resonant mode. Energy is fed back from collector circuit to emitter circuit via the crystal. Only at the series-resonant frequency of the crystal is the feedback path of low enough impedance to give the unity gain necessary for oscillation. The collector circuit is tuned to be resonant at the required frequency of oscillation to obtain the maximum gain from the transistor. Figs. 4.23 *a* and *b* show the circuits of two other types of crystal oscillator. Fig. 4.23*a* is the Pierce circuit and is a modification of a Colpitts oscillator in which the crystal takes the place of the inductor. The other oscillator circuit shown is the Miller circuit. The operation of these circuits and the function of their components are left as an exercise (4.13) for the reader.

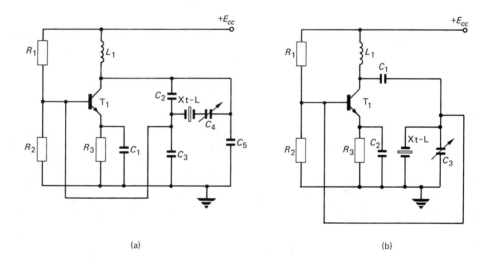

(a)   (b)

Fig. 4.23 (*a*) the Pierce and (*b*) the Miller crystal oscillators

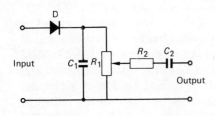

Fig. 4.24

Exercises

4.1. Briefly explain why it is necessary to include a detector stage in a receiver used for the reception of amplitude-modulated signals.

Describe, with the aid of a diagram, the operation of a semiconductor diode in the detection of an amplitude-modulated wave. *(C&G)*

4.2. (*a*) Explain how the input-voltage/output-current characteristic of a semiconductor diode is used to demodulate an amplitude-modulated wave.

(*b*) An amplitude modulated signal is applied to the input of the germanium diode detector shown in Fig. 4.24. By reference to current or voltage waveforms, describe the function of each circuit component in the detector. *(C&G)*

4.3. (*a*) Sketch the waveform of an amplitude-modulated carrier wave modulated to a depth of 40%. Label the axes to show the quantities involved. (*b*) With reference to your sketch explain what the envelope of the waveform represents. (*c*) Why is it necessary to include a detector stage in a radio receiver used for the reception of amplitude modulated signals? (*d*) State the relative advantages and disadvantages of thermionic and semiconductor diodes for use in such a detector stage. *(C&G)*

4.4. Draw the circuit diagram of a crystal-controlled transistor oscillator and explain its operation. List the factors which determine the frequency stability of such an oscillator. *(C&G)*

4.5. Draw the circuit of either a Colpitts or a Hartley oscillator using a junction transistor. Briefly describe its operation and give suitable component values if the required frequency is 1 MHz. List some of the factors which influence the frequency stability. *(C&G)*

4.6. Sketch a circuit diagram and describe the operation of an *LC* oscillator using a transistor. Give reasons for the particular configuration of transistor used, and indicate any features which improve stability of operation. *(C&G)*

4.7. (*a*) Draw a labelled diagram of a superheterodyne a.m. broadcast receiver and state the purpose of each stage. (*b*) For a detector stage (i) draw the circuit indicating typical component values, (ii) sketch the input and output waveforms. *(C&G)*

4.8. What are the advantages of operating an amplifier in push-pull? Draw the circuit diagram of a Class B push-pull amplifier indicating how bias is obtained. Explain, with the aid of suitable waveform diagrams, the operation of the circuit. Why is it necessary to have matched transistors? *(C&G)*

4.9. Draw the circuit diagram, including the driver stage, of a push-pull amplifier incorporating a complementary pair as the output stage. Describe the operation of the circuit. State two advantages of the circuit over one using transformers. *(C&G)*

4.10. Draw the circuit diagram of a two-stage tuned amplifier suitable for use in the i.f. amplifier section of a superheterodyne receiver. What are the main functions of this amplifier? Explain why (i) the collector tuned circuit is often tapped, and (ii) why the secondary winding of the coupling transformer is not always tuned. *(C&G)*

4.11. A tuned amplifier has a gain of 15 at its resonant (operating) frequency. How many identical stages must be connected in cascade to obtain an overall gain of at least 3000? What will be the overall gain at the 3 dB frequencies of a single stage?

4.12. Draw the circuit diagram of a transistor detector and describe its operation and the function of each component shown.

4.13. Draw the circuit diagram of a crystal oscillator and explain its method of operation. List the function of each component shown. Show clearly how the output voltage is taken from your circuit.

Short Exercises

4.14. What are the functions of a tuned radio-frequency amplifier? What is meant by the 3 dB bandwidth of an amplifier?

4.15. What is meant by ganging the stages of a tuned amplifier? When might ganging be desirable and what difficulties are associated with it?

4.16. Draw the circuit diagram of a tuned amplifier and explain the purpose of each component.

4.17. What are the differences between a radio-frequency amplifier and an intermediate-frequency amplifier for use in a super-heterodyne radio receiver?

4.18. Explain the difference between a linear and a non-linear detector.

4.19. Why must a detector stage be included in a radio receiver? What are the component frequencies present at the output of a diode detector?

4.20. The optimum load for the output transistor in a Class A, single-ended amplifier stage is 1000 ohms. What must be the turns ratio of the output transformer to match the transistor to a 8 ohm loudspeaker?

5 Radio Receivers

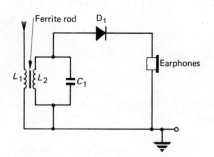

Fig. 5.1 Simple radio receiver

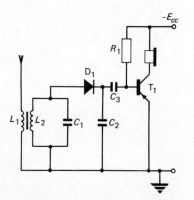

Fig. 5.2 Basic one-transistor radio receiver

Principles

The function of a radio receiver is: to select the wanted signal from all the signals picked up by the aerial, whilst rejecting all others; to extract the intelligence contained in the modulated signal; and to produce an audio-frequency output of sufficient power to operate the loudspeaker or other receiving device.

The circuit diagram of the simplest type of radio receiver is shown in Fig. 5.1. A wanted frequency can be selected from a number of frequencies by utilizing the selectivity characteristics of a parallel resonant circuit. In this receiver selection is obtained by adjusting capacitor C_1 to give resonance at the wanted signal frequency. The diode D_1 acts as a non-linear detector and extracts the audio-frequency signal, plus a number of other components, which is passed through the earphones for conversion into sound. A loudspeaker cannot be used because there is insufficient power. It may often be considered desirable to prevent the r.f. components of the detector output passing through the earphones; this is easily achieved by shunting the earphones with a suitable capacitor.

The a.f. output power of the simple receiver can be increased if an audio-frequency amplifier is used as in Fig. 5.2. The wanted signal is selected by the parallel-resonant circuit L_2C_1, and C_2 bypasses the r.f. components of the detected output. Capacitor C_3 presents the d.c. component of the detector output reaching the amplifier and upsetting the bias arrangements.

Further increase in the sound power delivered by the receiver could possibly be provided if a second and perhaps a third stage of a.f. gain were employed, but there are two snags with such a proposal. Firstly, the output signal-to-noise ratio may be rather poor and, secondly, distortion of the output waveform could be reduced if a linear diode detector were used instead of the non-linear detector. For a diode detector to work efficiently, with little distortion, the r.f. voltage applied to its input terminals should have a peak value of about 1 V.

A better method, therefore, of increasing the a.f. power output is to employ one or more stages of radio-frequency gain. The block schematic of a TUNED-RADIO-FREQUENCY (t.r.f.) radio receiver is shown in Fig. 5.3. The

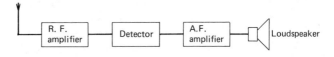

Fig. 5.3 The t.r.f. radio receiver

wanted signal frequency is selected by the tuned circuits in the r.f. amplifier, amplified and applied to the detector stage. If sufficient r.f. gain is provided, a diode detector can be employed; if not, some form of non-linear detection will still be required. The detected output is amplified by the a.f. amplifier to the level necessary to operate the loudspeaker.

Carrier frequencies in the medium and long wavebands are spaced at intervals of only 9 kHz, and a radio receiver must be capable of selecting one carrier frequency whilst rejecting the two immediately adjacent to it. To obtain the required selectivity, it is necessary to employ two or more resonant circuits in the r.f. stage, each of which must include a variable capacitor in order that the receiver can be tuned to receive signals on different carrier frequencies. If operation of the receiver is not to be too difficult, the tuned circuits must be arranged to that they can all be tuned by a single control knob. This requirement is normally satisfied by mounting all the tuning capacitors on the same spindle, when they are said to be *ganged*. Unfortunately, it is mechanically difficult to gang more than three or four capacitors and ensure that the associated stray capacitors are equal, and this number is rarely sufficient for adequate receiver selectivity.

The radio-frequency tuned circuits must be electrically isolated from one another and this means that the use of, say, four tuned circuits will require the use of a three-stage amplifier. The gain of a three-stage amplifier will be large and it will require only a small fraction of the output voltage to appear at the input of the first stage for oscillations to occur. Since the capacitances which tune the input and output circuits of the amplifier are mounted on the same spindle, it is extremely difficult to avoid the unwanted feedback.

Unwanted feedback of radio-frequency energy from one stage to another can also take place because of magnetic couplings. Magnetic inter-stage coupling can be avoided by mounting each stage within a metal case or *screen*. The magne-

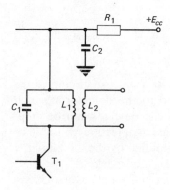

Fig. 5.4 Power supply decoupling

tic field set up by a stage will then induce an e.m.f. into the screen and cause eddy currents to flow. These eddy currents set up another magnetic flux that is in the opposite direction to the original flux and hence opposes it. As a result little, if any, magnetic field exists outside of the screened enclosure. If the screen is connected to earth it will also screen electric fields. The screening efficiency can be further increased by careful layout and by the use of screened wire or cable for the input and output connections.

It is also possible for individual stages to be coupled together by the impedance of the power supply. In order to reduce power supply coupling to a negligible level, it is customary to use a decoupling circuit. A simple decoupling circuit consists of a resistor connected in series with the power supply and a capacitor connected from the amplifier end of the resistor to earth, as shown in Fig. 5.4. Signal-frequency currents passing through the collector tuned circuit are presented with a low-impedance path via C_2 to earth or a higher-impedance route through R_1 and the power supply earth; thus the signal-frequency currents do not enter the power supply. The disadvantage of the decoupling circuit is, of course, the d.c. voltage drop across the series resistor R_1 which reduces the collector supply voltage of the stage.

A further disadvantage of the t.r.f. receiver is associated with the need for radio-frequency amplifier stages that can be tuned to different frequencies. The gain and selectivity of a tuned amplifier stage is determined by the impedance/frequency characteristics of its collector tuned circuit. The impedance at resonance of a parallel-tuned circuit is L/Cr ohms and its resonant frequency is $f = 1/2\pi\sqrt{(LC)}$ Hz. Since the resonant voltage gain depends on the L/C ratio, the performance of an amplifier stage depends upon whether tuning is carried out by means of a variable capacitor or a variable inductor. If the stage is to be tuned to a higher frequency, then either the capacitance or the inductance of the tuned circuit must be reduced. If the capacitance is reduced, the gain at resonance will be increased, but if the inductance is reduced the resonant gain will be decreased. Changing the L/C ratio also affects the shape of the gain/frequency characteristic of a stage. Increase in L/C raises the whole curve but lifts the peak more than the sides; that is, an increase in the L/C ratio increases both resonant gain and the selectivity. In a t.r.f. receiver these effects are undesirable since it is usually required to have the same gain at all operating frequencies. Further, the use of several stages in cascade results in bandwidth shrinkage.

The Superheterodyne Radio Receiver

All the difficulties associated with a t.r.f. radio receiver would be easier to overcome if most of the necessary gain and selectivity could be provided at a fixed frequency. This is the principle of the type of radio receiver most commonly employed—the SUPERHETERODYNE radio receiver.

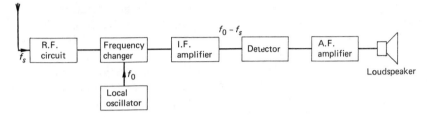

Fig. 5.5 The superheterodyne radio receiver

The basic block schematic of a superheterodyne radio receiver is shown in Fig. 5.5; its method of operation is briefly as follows. The wanted signal, at frequency f_s, is passed by the r.f. stage and applied to the mixer or frequency changer together with the output voltage of the local oscillator, at frequency f_0. One of the products of the mixing process is the difference frequency, either $f_s - f_0$ or $f_0 - f_s$ according to which frequency is the higher. The difference frequency is known as the IN-TERMEDIATE FREQUENCY (i.f.) and is selected by the i.f. amplifier and amplified. The i.f. amplifier employs highly-selective coupled tuned circuits, or *i.f. transformers*, to obtain the necessary gain/frequency characteristic. The modulated output of the i.f. amplifier is detected and the recovered a.f. voltage is amplified by the a.f. amplifier to the level required to operate the loudspeaker.

The i.f. amplifier operates at a fixed frequency and is tuned by the manufacturer and is easily screened to reduce feedback to such an extent that instability is avoided. This makes it relatively easy to provide the necessary gain and selectivity.

Choice of Local Oscillator Frequency

The intermediate frequency of a superheterodyne radio receiver is the difference between the wanted signal frequency and the local oscillator frequency. Two possibilities exist: the local oscillator frequency can be higher than the signal frequency, or vice versa.

Consider a receiver with an intermediate frequency of 465 kHz that is tunable over the medium frequency band 525 KHz to 1605 kHz. If the frequency of the local oscillator is higher than the wanted signal frequency the oscillator must be tunable from $(525 + 465) = 990$ kHz to $(1605 + 465) = 2070$ kHz, a frequency ratio of 2070/990, or 2.091 : 1. Such a frequency ratio would require the use of a variable capacitor having a ratio maximum-capacitance/minimum-capacitance of $(2.091)^2$, or 4.372 : 1. Such a capacitance ratio is easily obtained.

The alternative is to make the signal frequency higher than the local oscillator frequency. The oscillator frequency must then be variable from $(525 - 465) = 60$ kHz to $(1605 - 465) = 1140$ kHz. This is a frequency ratio of 1140/60, or 19 : 1 and requires a capacitance ratio of $(19)^2$, or 361 : 1. Such a large capacitance ratio could not be obtained with a single variable capacitor and would not be easy or cheap to achieve. It is therefore usual to make the local oscillator frequency higher than the wanted signal frequency, i.e.

$$f_0 = f_s + f_i \tag{5.1}$$

The sum frequency component of the mixer output is not chosen for the intermediate frequency because it would mean that the i.f. would have to be greater than the highest frequency in the tuning range of the receiver. The various factors leading to the choice of intermediate frequency will be discussed later; here it is enough to notice that use of the sum frequency would prevent the use of the optimum intermediate frequency.

Many communication receivers cover a number of frequency bands in the medium and high frequency bands, and are tunable from approximately 1.6 MHz to 30 MHz. The local oscillator frequency must again be chosen to be higher than the signal frequency. Receivers operating in the v.h.f. and u.h.f. bands may have their oscillator frequency either lower or higher than the tunable signal frequency band. For example, an f.m. broadcast receiver tunes over the frequency band 87.5 MHz to 100 MHz and uses an intermediate frequency of 10.7 MHz. If the local oscillator frequency is chosen to be higher than the signal frequency, the required capacitance ratio is 1.271 : 1, while if the signal frequency is higher than the oscillator frequency the capacitance ratio demanded is 1.352 : 1. Clearly, there is very little difference between the two capacitance ratios.

Image Channel Interference

No matter what frequency a superheterodyne receiver is tuned to, there is always another frequency that will also produce the intermediate frequency. This other frequency is known as the IMAGE FREQUENCY. The image signal has a frequency f_{im} such that the difference between it and the local oscillator frequency is equal to the intermediate frequency f_i, i.e.

$$f_i = f_{im} - f_0$$

Substituting for f_0 from eqn. (5.1),

$$f_i = f_{im} - (f_s + f_i)$$

or

$$f_{im} = f_s + 2f_i \qquad (5.2)$$

The image signal is thus separated from the wanted signal by twice the intermediate frequency. The image signal must be prevented from reaching the mixer or it will produce an interference signal which, since it is at the intermediate frequency, cannot be eliminated by the selectivity of the i.f. amplifier. The r.f. stage must include a resonant circuit with sufficient selectivity to reject the image signal when tuned to the wanted signal frequency. Tuning is necessary because the wanted signal frequency, and hence the image signal frequency, will vary. It is not difficult to obtain a resonant circuit with good enough selectivity to accept the wanted signal and reject the image signal when their separation is an appreciable fraction of the wanted signal frequency. As the signal frequency is increased, the fractional frequency separation becomes smaller and the image rejection less efficient.

Any vestige of the image signal reaching the mixer will produce a signal appearing as crosstalk at the output of the receiver. If a signal at a few kilohertz away from the image signal should reach the mixer, the two i.f. signals produced would beat together to produce a whistle at the output of the receiver.

The *image response ratio* is the ratio, in decibels, of the voltages at the wanted signal and image signal frequencies necessary at the receiver input terminals to produce the same audio output.

EXAMPLE 5.1

A superheterodyne radio receiver has an intermediate frequency of 465 kHz and is tuned to 1065 kHz. Calculate (*a*) the frequency of the local oscillator, and (*b*) the frequency of the image signal.

Solution
From eqn. (5.1),

$$f_0 = 1065 + 465 = 1530 \text{ kHz} \qquad (Ans.)$$

and from eqn.(5.2)

$$f_{im} = 1065 + 930 = 1995 \text{ kHz} \qquad (Ans.)$$

Ganging and Tracking

For a superheterodyne radio receiver to receive a given signal frequency it is necessary for the radio-frequency amplifier to be tuned to the signal frequency f_s (mainly to reject the image frequency), and for the local oscillator to be tuned to a frequency $f_i + f_s$ where f_i is the intermediate frequency. To permit tuning of the receiver with a single tuning control, the variable capacitors forming a part of the r.f. and oscillator resonant circuits are mounted on a single spindle, or GANGED. Since the frequencies at which the r.f. and oscillator circuits operate are different, ganging does not cause instability. The maintenance of a constant frequency difference between the radio-frequency and oscillator circuits is known as TRACKING. It is difficult to arrange for correct tracking to be very nearly maintained over the whole of the tuning range of the receiver. The usual way of arranging adequate tracking is to provide identical values of tuning capacitance in the r.f. and oscillator circuits and to use a lower value of inductance in the oscillator circuit than in the r.f. circuit. It is also found to be necessary to fit series and shunt capacitances, known respectively as *padder* and *trimmer* capacitors, as shown in Fig. 5.6.

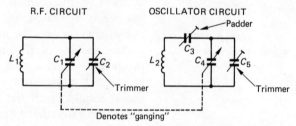

Fig. 5.6 The use of the trimmer and padder capacitors

The padder and trimmer capacitors are required to minimize the tracking error as the receiver is tuned over the whole of the tuning range. This is illustrated by the curves given in Fig. 5.7. The ideal curve shows the condition in which the frequency difference between the oscillator and signal frequency circuits is always equal to the intermediate frequency, assumed to be 465 kHz.

Adjacent Channel Selectivity

The spacing between the carrier frequencies allocated to different transmitters is limited by the available frequency spectrum, e.g. 9 kHz for sound broadcast transmitters in the medium waveband in Europe. The SELECTIVITY of a radio receiver is its ability to reject signals at carrier frequencies adjacent to the wanted signal carrier frequency. The selectivity is mainly determined by the gain/frequency characteristic of the i.f. amplifier.

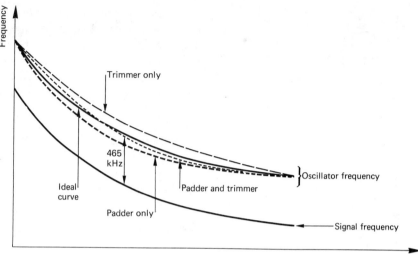

Fig. 5.7 Tracking curves

The ADJACENT CHANNEL RATIO is the ratio, in decibels, of the input voltages at the wanted and adjacent channel frequencies for the adjacent channel to produce an output power 30 dB smaller than the output power of the signal frequency.

EXAMPLE 5.2

A superheterodyne receiver is tuned to a certain frequency at which an input voltage of 10 μV produces an output power of 50 mW. If the signal voltage required at the adjacent channel frequency to produce 30 dB less output power is 1 mV, calculate the adjacent channel ratio.

$$\text{Adjacent channel ratio} = 20 \log_{10}\left(\frac{1 \times 10^{-3}}{10 \times 10^{-6}}\right) = 40 \text{ dB} \qquad (Ans.)$$

Sensitivity

The SENSITIVITY of a radio receiver is its ability to receive very small signals and produce an output of satisfactory signal-to-noise ratio. It is usually expressed as the minimum input signal, modulated 30% at 1000 Hz required to produce 50 mW output power with a signal-to-noise ratio of 15 dB. It is necessary to include signal-to-noise ratio in the measurement of sensitivity because it would otherwise be possible for the output power to consist mainly of useless noise.

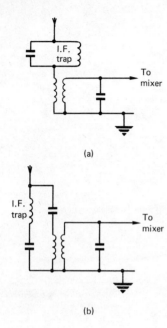

(a)

(b)

Fig. 5.8 I.F. traps

I.F. Breakthrough

If a signal at the intermediate frequency is picked up by an aerial and allowed to reach the mixer, it will reach the i.f. amplifier and interfere with the wanted signal. Such a signal must therefore be suppressed in the r.f. stage by an I.F. TRAP (see Fig. 5.8). The i.f. trap consists of either a parallel-resonant circuit, tuned to the intermediate frequency, connected in series with the aerial lead (Fig. 5.8a) or a series-resonant circuit, also tuned to the intermediate frequency, connected between the aerial lead and earth (Fig. 5.8b). In the first circuit the i.f. trap has a high impedance and blocks the passage of the unwanted i.f. signal; in the second circuit the i.f. trap has a low impedance and shunts the unwanted signal to earth.

Other Sources of Interference

A superheterodyne receiver is also exposed to a number of other sources of interference. *Co-channel interference* is due to another signal at the same frequency and cannot be eliminated by the receiver itself. When it occurs it is the result of unusual propagation conditions making it possible for transmissions from a distant (geographically) station to be picked up by the aerial. Harmonics of the local oscillator frequency may combine with unwanted stations, or with harmonics produced by the mixer, to produce various difference frequency components, some of which may fall within the passband of the i.f. amplifier. It is also possible for two r.f. signals arriving at the input to the mixer to beat together and produce a component at the intermediate frequency.

Local Oscillator Radiation

The local oscillator operates at a radio frequency and may well radiate either directly or by coupling to the aerial. Direct radiation is limited by screening the oscillator, and radiation from the aerial is reduced by using an r.f. amplifier to prevent the oscillator voltage reaching the aerial. Radiation of the local oscillator frequency does not have a detrimental effect on the receiver in which it originates but is a source of interference to other nearby receivers.

EXAMPLE 5.3

A superheterodyne radio receiver has an intermediate frequency of 465 kHz and is tuned to receive an unmodulated carrier at 1200 kHz. Calculate the frequency of the audio output signal if present at the mixer input there are also (*a*) a 1208 kHz, and (*b*) a 462 kHz sinusoidal signal.

Solution
(a) The local oscillator frequency is $465 + 1200 = 1665$ kHz, and hence the 1208 kHz signal produces a difference frequency output from the mixer of $1665 - 1208 = 457$ kHz. If the i.f. bandwidth is only 9 kHz on 465 kHz, the 457 KHz signal will be rejected.
(b) The 462 kHz signal will appear at the mixer output and will be passed by the i.f. amplifier and will beat with the 465 kHz signal to produce a 3 kHz tone at the receiver output.

Choice of Intermediate Frequency

The main factors to be considered when choosing the intermediate frequency for a superheterodyne radio receiver are (a) the required i.f. bandwidth, (b) interference signals, (c) the required i.f. gain and stability, and (d) the required adjacent channel selectivity.

The minimum bandwidth demanded of an i.f. amplifier depends upon the type of receiver and is about 9 kHz for an amplitude-modulation broadcast receiver. Since the bandwidth of a coupled-tuned circuit is proportional to its resonant frequency, the larger the bandwidth required the higher must be the intermediate frequency. The intermediate frequency should not lie within the tuning range of the receiver, so that the r.f. stage can include an i.f. trap to prevent i.f. interference. However, to simplify the design and construction of the i.f. amplifier the intermediate frequency should be as low as possible. Adequate adjacent channel selectivity is easier to obtain using a low intermediate frequency, but on the other hand, image channel rejection is easier if a high intermediate frequency is selected.

The intermediate frequency chosen for a receiver must be a compromise between these conflicting factors. Most amplitude-modulated broadcast receivers employ an intermediate frequency of between 450 and 470 kHz; a.m. communication receivers often make use of a 1.4 MHz intermediate frequency but frequency-modulation broadcast receivers, which require an i.f. bandwidth of about 200 kHz, use an intermediate-frequency of 10.7 MHz.

Use of an R.F. Amplifier

At frequencies up to about 5 MHz or so the noise picked up by an aerial is much larger than the noise generated within the receiver (which originates mainly in the frequency-changer stage). An r.f. amplifier will amplify the aerial noise as well as the signal and produce little, if any, improvement in signal-to-noise ratio. At higher frequencies the aerial noise decreases and the noise generated by the frequency changer is predominant; the use of r.f. amplification will then improve the signal-to-noise ratio of the receiver. An r.f. amplifier also isolates the local oscillator from the aerial and considerably reduces local oscillator radiation. Including an r.f. amplifier allows two or more tuned circuits to be used, with a consequent improvement in image rejection.

Generally, amplitude-modulation medium-wave broadcast receivers are not provided with an r.f. amplifier whilst receivers, of all types, operating at higher frequencies do incorporate one or more stages of r.f. gain.

Automatic Gain Control

The signals arriving at the input terminals of a radio receiver are subject to continual fading, and unless AUTOMATIC GAIN CONTROL (a.g.c.) is used, the volume control will require continual adjustment to keep the output of the receiver more or less constant. The function of an a.g.c. system is to vary the gain of a receiver to maintain a reasonably constant output power even though there are large variations in the input signal level. Thus the gain of the receiver must be reduced by the a.g.c. system when a large-amplitude input signal is received, and increased for a small input signal. The variation in the receiver gain also serves to prevent the output level changing overmuch as the receiver is tuned from one station to another, and it also avoids a.f. amplifier distortion caused by over-loading on larger input signals.

The a.g.c. circuitry in radio receivers is beyond the scope of this book, but the basic principle is as follows. A direct voltage is developed by the a.g.c. circuit that is proportional to the *carrier* level (*not* the side-frequency level) at the output of the i.f. amplifier. This voltage is fed back to one or more of the r.f., mixer and i.f. stages to supplement the bias arrangements of each stage (Fig. 5.9). The circuitry is so arranged that an increase in bias voltage reduces the gain of each of the controlled stages.

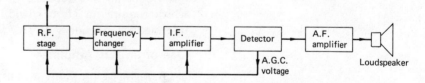

Fig. 5.9 Application of automatic gain control to a receiver

With *simple a.g.c.* a control voltage is developed, and the gain of the receiver reduced, immediately a carrier voltage is present at the output of the i.f amplifier. It is desirable, though, that the full receiver gain should be available for very weak signals, and so *delayed a.g.c.* is often employed. Delayed a.g.c. is arranged so that an a.g.c. voltage is not developed until the input signal has reached a predetermined value,

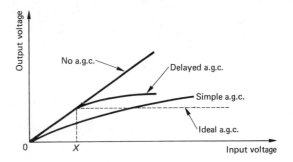

Fig. 5.10 A.G.C. characteristics

usually that at which the full power output of the audio amplifier can be obtained.

Output/input characteristics for a radio receiver having (*a*) no a.g.c., (*b*) simple a.g.c., and (*c*) delayed a.g.c. are shown in Fig. 5.10. The ideal a.g.c. system should not operate until the input signal reaches a predetermined level *x*, and would thereafter keep the output of the receiver constant (dotted line in Fig. 5.10). The effects of selective fading are not reduced by the use of a.g.c.—indeed the converse is true. When selective fading is present the carrier may well fade at an instant when one or both sidebands have increased in value. This will produce an increase in receiver gain and accentuate the selective fading. Similarly, the gain of the receiver may be reduced by an increase in carrier level at an instant when one or both sidebands have faded.

Functions of Stages

The operation of a superheterodyne radio receiver can be summarized by listing the functions of each of the stages shown in Fig. 5.9:

(*a*) *R.F. Stage.* Suppresses the image signal and signals at or near the intermediate frequency. Couples the aerial to the receiver and reduces local oscillator radiation. May provide amplification of the signal and an improvement in the signal-to-noise ratio.

(*b*) *Frequency-changer.* Converts the wanted signal frequency to the intermediate frequency.

(*c*) *I.F. Amplifier.* Provides most of the gain and selectivity of the receiver.

(*d*) *Detector.* Extracts the a.f. intelligence from the modulated output of the i.f. amplifier and produces the a.g.c. voltage.

(*e*) *A.F. Amplifier.* Amplifies the detected output to provide sufficient power to operate the loudspeaker.

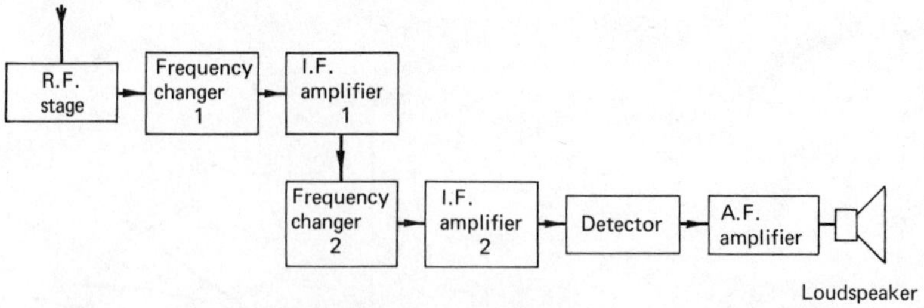

Fig. 5.11 Double-superheterodyne receiver

Double Superheterodyne Receivers

The intermediate frequency of a superheterodyne radio receiver is chosen as a compromise between the various factors discussed earlier. At the higher end of the m.f. band and in the h.f. band the image signal is only a small percentage off-tune and it may well be difficult to obtain adequate rejection. One way out of this difficulty is to employ the *double superheterodyne principle*, illustrated by the block diagram of Fig. 5.11. The wanted signal is picked up by the aerial and is amplified by the r.f. stage before arriving at the first frequency changer. The first intermediate frequency may be made as high as is necessary to obtain the required image rejection; for example, a receiver operating in the h.f. band might have a first i.f. of 4 MHz. The first local oscillator must be of variable frequency in order that the wanted signal frequency can always be translated into the first intermediate frequency. The frequency of the second local oscillator is fixed because the input to the second changer is always at the same frequency. The second intermediate frequency is chosen primarily to give adequate adjacent channel selectivity, and is often about 100 kHz.

EXAMPLE 5.4

A double superheterodyne receiver has intermediate frequencies of 4 MHz and 100 kHz and is tuned to receive a signal at 20 MHz. Calculate the frequencies of the first and second local oscillators.

$$f_{o1} = f_s + f_{i1} = 20 + 4 = 24 \text{ MHz} \qquad (Ans.)$$
$$f_{o2} = f_{i1} + f_{i2} = 4000 + 100 = 4100 \text{ kHz} \qquad (Ans.)$$

Communication Receivers

The term *communication receiver* is often applied to a receiver that has been designed to receive signals in a number of different frequency bands, and may or may not be of the double-superheterodyne type. To minimize noise and interference it is desirable to use the minimum bandwidth possible for

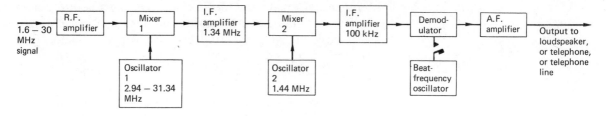

Fig. 5.12 Communications receiver

each type of received signal, and some means of varying the i.f. bandwidth is generally provided. Some receivers also have provision for the reception of narrow-band telegraphy signals.

The block schematic diagram of a typical communication radio receiver is shown in Fig. 5.12. The frequency coverage of the receiver is split into four different frequency bands (1.6–4 MHz, 4–10 MHz, 10–20 MHz, and 20–30 MHz) by switching into the r.f. amplifier, the mixer 1 and the oscillator 1 circuits different values of inductance. The use of different inductors is necessary because a variable capacitor would not be able to provide the necessarily large capacitance ratio associated with a single value of inductance. The second i.f. amplifier operates at the fixed frequency of 100 kHz and is provided with a variable selectivity facility. Any one of five different selectivities, ranging from 400 Hz up to 8000 Hz, can be chosen by switching into circuit different crystal filters. Alternatively, different bandwidths may be obtained by switching different values of resistance across the inductance of the coupled tuned circuits used in the final i.f. stage.

Variable selectivity is often provided with communications receivers so that the bandwidth appropriate for a particular service can be selected. For example, the reception of sound broadcast signals will require the largest bandwidth of 8 kHz, while for the reception of speech the narrowest bandwidth that can be used without intelligibility being lost will reduce both noise and adjacent-channel interference. The narrow bandwidth of 400 Hz is used when C.W. telegraph signals are to be received.

For the reception of C.W. radio-telegraphy Morse-code signals a tunable beat-frequency oscillator is switched into circuit. The signal appearing at the output of the second i.f. amplifier consists of the presence, or the absence, of the unmodulated 100 kHz carrier to represent the dots, dashes, and spaces of the Morse code. The detector in a radio receiver is designed to respond to the modulation of the carrier and so produces zero output when a C.W. signal is applied to its input terminals. To make the Morse code signal audible it is necessary to beat the 100 kHz carrier output of the final i.f. amplifier with the output of the beat frequency oscillator. The *beating* process will produce a component at a frequency equal to the difference between the carrier and beat-frequency oscillator frequencies. By suitable choice of the frequency of the beat-frequency oscillator the difference frequency can be arranged to fall within the passband of the audio amplifier.

Exercises

5.1. Describe, with the aid of a schematic diagram, the functions of the various stages of a communication type of superheterodyne radio receiver. Briefly explain how alternate bandwidths of 12, 5, 1 and 0.1 kHz could be obtained. *(C & G)*

5.2. A radio receiver has an intermediate frequency of 450 kHz, and is tuned to receive a station radiating on a frequency of 1400 kHz. At what frequency will i.f. breakthrough occur? What is the minimum r.f. bandwidth necessary if the highest modulating frequency used at the transmitter is 6 kHz? Calculate the image frequency. How may the image ratio be improved? *(C & G)*

5.3. Draw a block schematic diagram to show the arrangement of a superheterodyne radio receiver, briefly explaining the function of each stage. By means of a numerical example illustrate the advantage of the double superheterodyne principle for the reception of a signal at a frequency of 14 MHz. *(C & G)*

5.4. Draw a block diagram of a communication-type superheterodyne radio receiver and briefly explain the function of each stage. Discuss any inherent disadvantage of the superheterodyne principle. *(C & G)*

5.5. Sketch, on squared paper, the waveform of a high-frequency wave amplitude-modulated by a 1 kHz sinewave, for depths of (*a*) 20% and (*b*) 60%. The unmodulated carrier wave has an r.m.s. value of 0.7 V.

Explain briefly what bandwidth would be required in (*a*) the r.f. stages, (*b*) the i.f. stages, (*c*) the audio stages of a superheterodyne radio receiver if it is required to receive an amplitude-modulated signal in which the highest modulating frequency used is 4.5 kHz. *(C & G)*

5.6. Draw a block diagram of a superheterodyne receiver. Explain the terms *adjacent channel selectivity* and *image rejection*, and briefly explain which parts of the receiver principally determine its performance in each of these respects. If a receiver has an intermediate frequency of 450 kHz, calculate the image frequency when it is tuned to a signal of 1400 kHz. *(C & G)*

5.7. Draw a block diagram of a superheterodyne general-purpose communication receiver and briefly explain the function of each stage. Explain the principal advantages of adding an r.f. amplifier stage. *(C & G)*

5.8. Draw a block diagram of a superheterodyne communication radio receiver. State the main factors which govern (*a*) the choice of intermediate frequency, (*b*) the use of a radio-frequency amplifying stage, (*c*) the intermediate-frequency bandwidth.

Explain briefly the following terms (i) image channel rejection, (ii) adjacent-channel selectivity, (iii) delayed automatic gain control. (*C & G*)

5.9. (*a*) Define the following terms used in superheterodyne reception: (i) image or second channel reception, (ii) adjacent channel selectivity, (iii) frequency changer. (*b*) Explain where in the superheterodyne receiver image channel rejection and adjacent channel selectivity are most effectively obtained. (*c*) Why is a frequency changing process used? (*C & G*)

5.10. (*a*) With the aid of a block diagram explain the operation of a superheterodyne receiver. (*b*) State with reasons two principal requirements for each of the following stages in a superheterodyne receiver: (i) radio-frequency, (ii) frequency changer, (iii) intermediate frequency, (iv) audio frequency, (v) output. (*C & G*)

Short Exercises

5.11. Draw the block diagram of a t.r.f. receiver. List its shortcomings.

5.12. Explain the difficulties associated with the ganging of multiple r.f. amplifier stages.

5.13. Explain why it necessary to employ screening and decoupling between r.f. amplifier stages working at the same frequency.

5.14. List the factors which influence the choice of intermediate frequency for a superheterodyne radio receiver. Quote typical values of intermediate frequency.

5.15. What is meant by the term image signal used in conjunction with a superheterodyne radio receiver? How is this signal prevented from reaching the mixer stage?

5.16. Draw the block schematic diagram of (i) t.r.f. receiver and (ii) a superheterodyne receiver. What are the advantages of the superheterodyne receiver?

5.17. List the functions of each of the stages of a superheterodyne radio receiver.

5.18. (*a*) How is the required signal frequency converted to the intermediate frequency in a superheterodyne receiver? (*b*) What are the advantages of providing a r.f. amplifier stage in a superheterodyne radio receiver?

5.19. What is meant by (i) simple automatic gain control and (ii) delayed automatic gain control? Why are they used?

5.20. List the differences between a broadcast receiver and a communication receiver.

5.21. What is meant by the double superheterodyne principle and why is it sometimes used?

6 Radio Transmitters

Introduction

The function of a radio transmitter in a communication system is to translate the audio-frequency signal to the required part of the frequency spectrum and to amplify the signal to the wanted radiated power level. A radio transmitter may employ amplitude or frequency modulation to achieve the necessary frequency translation and if amplitude modulation is used it may be double, single, or independent sideband. Medium-frequency broadcast transmitters operate at a fixed frequency but a high-frequency broadcast transmitter might be able to operate on two or more fixed frequencies. As propagation conditions in the ionosphere vary, it will often be necessary to change the operating frequency of a high-frequency radio-telephony link in order to maintain service. High-frequency communication transmitters must therefore be capable of rapid frequency changes. In this book only high-frequency amplitude-modulation transmitters are considered.

Radio-frequency Power Amplifiers

Class A operation of an amplifier is adopted because of the low signal distortion it can offer. The maximum theoretical efficiency with which the d.c. power taken from the power supply is converted into a.c. signal power output is, however, only 50%, and practical efficiencies are lower than this—particularly in the case of thermionic valve amplifiers. To obtain a greater efficiency than this, an amplifier may be operated under either Class B or Class C conditions.

With Class B operation (see Fig. 6.1), the operating point is set at cut-off. The output current flows only during alternate half-cycles of the signal waveform. It is evident that the output current waveform is highly distorted; Class B bias can there-

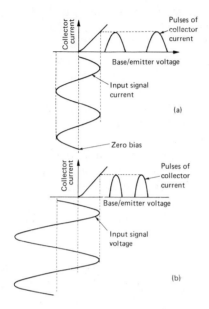

Fig. 6.1 Class B and Class C bias

fore only be employed with circuits that are able to restore the missing half-cycles of the signal waveform. Such circuits are known as "push-pull" amplifiers and "tuned-radio frequency" amplifiers. Class B operation has a maximum theoretical efficiency of 78.5%.

Even greater efficiency can be obtained with Class C bias. With Class C bias, shown in Fig. 6.1, the operating point is set well beyond cut-off. The output current flows in the form of a series of narrow pulses having a duration which is less than half the periodic time of the input signal waveform. Class C bias is used with radio-frequency power amplifiers because the anode efficiency can be very high, perhaps as much as 80%. Such a high efficiency is extremely important when high-power applications are concerned. For example, to obtain an output power of 60 kW an input power of 75 kW is required if the efficiency is 80%, but the input power must be 85.7 kW when the efficiency is reduced to 70%. High power transmitters employ the thermionic valve Class C circuit in their final high power stages although some, if not all, of the earlier stages are likely to use transistors. Modern low-power transmitters are often completely transistorized.

The basic circuit diagram of a CLASS C RADIO-FREQUENCY POWER AMPLIFIER is shown in Figs. 6.2a and b. A triode valve is shown in both circuits but, in practice, many transmitters use tetrodes. The difference between the two circuits lies in the way in which the anode-tuned circuit is connected; in the series-feed circuit of Fig. 6.2a the tuned circuit is connected in series with the h.t. supply, while in the parallel-feed circuit of Fig. 6.2b the tuned circuit is isolated from the power supply. The parallel feed circuit requires two extra components, namely C_2 and L_4. C_2 prevents the tuned

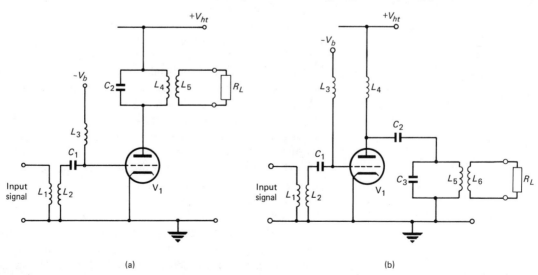

Fig. 6.2 Class C power amplifiers

circuit inductance L_5 completing a low-resistance path to earth for the d.c. current taken from the power supply. Inductor L_4 prevents signal-frequency currents passing into the power supply instead of into the tuned circuit. In both circuits the valve is biased to operate under Class C conditions by the negative bias voltage V_b which is applied via inductor L_3; the function of L_3 is to prevent signal-frequency currents being shunted, via the bias supply, to earth. Capacitor C_1 is required to prevent the bias supply being shorted to earth by L_2.

Since the valve is biased well beyond the cut-off point, anode current will flow only during the peaks of the positive half cycles of the input signal voltage when the signal voltage is larger than the bias voltage (see Fig. 6.3). With a triode it is usual for the signal voltage to take the grid potential positive with respect to the cathode at its positive half-cycle peaks. This practice results in the flow of grid current but in particular it results in a larger anode current than would otherwise be possible. A tetrode valve has a greater gain than has a triode, and sufficient anode current can be obtained without recourse to driving the grid positive. Hence tetrode Class C circuits are not operated with grid current. The anode current flows in a series of pulses each of which lasts for a period of time that is less than half of the periodic time of the signal voltage. The anode current is clearly not of sinusoidal waveform and contains components at a number of different frequencies. These frequencies are the frequency of the signal voltage applied to the grid of the valve, and a number of harmonics of that frequency. The fundamental frequency component has the greatest amplitude. The anode circuit is tuned to be resonant at the signal frequency. The impedance of a parallel-resonant circuit reaches its maximum value at its frequency of resonance and is also then purely resistive. At all other frequencies the impedance of the anode circuit is much smaller and is not a pure resistance. The voltage developed across the anode tuned circuit is therefore only at the signal frequency and is of sinusoidal waveform. The voltage developed across the anode circuit is directly proportional to the h.t. supply voltage. Fig. 6.3 shows the waveforms of the anode and grid voltages and currents in a Class C tuned r.f. power amplifier. Notice that the grid and anode voltages are in antiphase with one another and that the grid current flows for a shorter period of time than does the anode current.

Although the circuit diagrams given in Fig. 6.2 show the required grid bias provided from a separate bias voltage source V_b, many circuits employ *leaky-grid bias* (see EII). When a triode valve is used, unwanted feedback of energy from the anode circuit to the grid circuit may lead to instability unless a *neutralizing* circuit is added to counteract the feedback. The

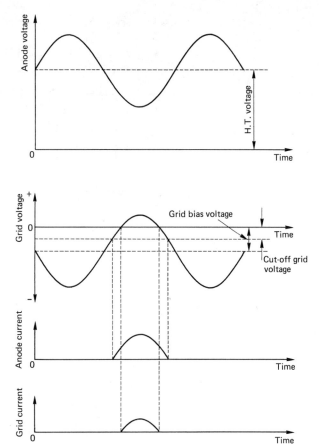

Fig. 6.3 Current and voltage waveforms in a Class C amplifier

tetrode does not suffer from this disadvantage because of its much smaller anode-grid interelectrode capacitance. On the other hand, the triode possesses the important advantages of greater efficiency and better linearity. Both types of valve must be provided with some means of removing heat from the anode arising because of the power dissipated there, but with the tetrode the problem is made worse by the need to remove heat from the screen grid as well.

To avoid the need for neutralization circuitry, triodes are often operated in the *earthed grid* configuration; the earthed grid now acts as an efficient screen between the input and the output circuits. The circuit diagram of an earthed-grid Class C radio-frequency power amplifier is given in Fig. 6.4. The functions of the components are similar to those in the circuits of Fig. 6.2, but note that the bias voltage V_b is now a positive potential.

An increased power output can be obtained from a given type of valve if two valves are used in a Class C push-pull amplifier. Fig. 6.5 shows the circuit diagram.

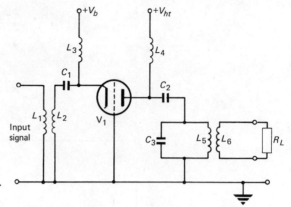

Fig. 6.4 Earthed-grid Class C power amplifier

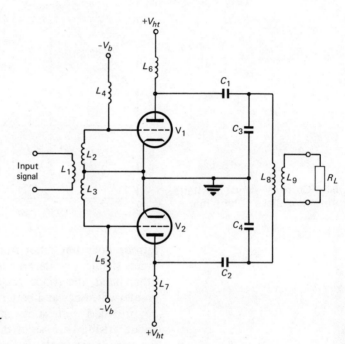

Fig. 6.5 Push-pull Class C power amplifier

A Class C tuned amplifier can only be used to amplify signals of constant amplitude, it cannot amplify amplitude-modulated signals without considerable distortion. To amplify an amplitude-modulated wave, a Class B tuned amplifier must be used. The circuit diagram of a Class B tuned amplifier is the same as the Class C circuits shown in Fig. 6.2, the difference between the amplifiers lying in the value of the grid bias voltage. The maximum theoretical efficiency of a Class B circuit is 78.5% but practical efficiencies are some 50–60%.

Frequency Multipliers

The anode current of a Class C tuned amplifier flows in a series of less than half-sinewave pulses and contains components at the input signal frequency and harmonics of that frequency. If the anode circuit is tuned to be resonant at a harmonic of the signal frequency, the voltage developed across the load will be at that harmonic frequency. Thus if the anode is tuned to the third harmonic of the input frequency, the circuit will multiply the input frequency by a factor of three. The magnitude of the output voltage that can be obtained from a frequency multiplier decreases as the order of the harmonic to which the circuit is tuned is increased. In practice, the highest multiplication factor used is 5; when a greater degree of frequency multiplication is required two or more multipliers are connected in cascade.

Amplitude-modulated Class C Tuned Amplifiers

The output voltage of a Class C tuned amplifier is directly proportional to the value of the h.t. supply voltage applied to the circuit. If, therefore, the h.t. supply can be made to vary in accordance with the characteristics of the modulating signal, an amplitude-modulated waveform would be obtained. This can be achieved by introducing the modulating signal into the anode circuit in series with the supply voltage. The basic circuit diagram of an *anode-modulated Class C tuned amplifier* is shown in Fig. 6.6.

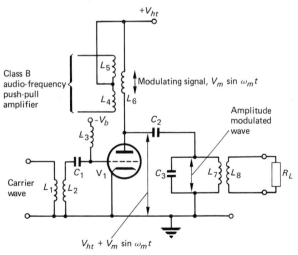

Fig. 6.6 Anode-modulated Class C power amplifier

The output voltage of an audio-frequency Class B push-pull amplifier is coupled into the anode circuit of V_1 via the mutual inductance between L_4/L_5 and L_6. The modulating signal voltage is then inserted in series with the d.c. supply voltage so that the effective supply voltage applied to the valve is the sum of the modulating and supply voltages, i.e. $V_{ht} + V_m \sin \omega t$. The peak voltage developed across the tuned circuit $C_3 L_7$ is directly proportional to the effective supply voltage and hence it varies with the same waveform as the modulating signal, i.e. it is amplitude modulated.

The Class B *modulating* stage must be capable of providing a sufficiently large output voltage to vary the supply voltage to the extent necessary for a desired depth of modulation to be achieved. For 80% modulation, for example, the peak modulating signal voltage in the anode circuit must equal $0.8\ V_{ht}$.

Amplitude-modulation Transmitters

The basic principle of an amplitude-modulation transmitter is that the carrier wave is derived from a high-stability oscillator, often of the crystal type, and is amplified, and sometimes frequency multiplied as well, by a number of radio-frequency amplifiers until the desired output level and frequency are achieved. At some stage in the transmitter the carrier wave must be amplitude modulated by the audio-frequency signal. The modulation process can be carried out at the final amplifier stage where the carrier is at its final power level, or it can be carried out at a low-level stage and then the modulated wave must be amplified to the required power level. The two basic types of transmitter are known respectively as high-level and low-level transmitters.

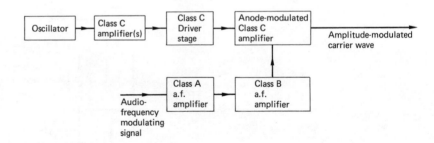

Fig. 6.7 High-level amplitude-modulation transmitter

The basic block schematic diagram of a HIGH-LEVEL TRANSMITTER is shown in Fig. 6.7. The carrier frequency is generated by a crystal oscillator and is amplified to the required transmitter output level by a number of cascaded Class C tuned power amplifiers. The function of the driver stage is to produce a sufficiently large voltage at the input terminals of the final stage to ensure that the anode current pulses attain an amplitude such that the required carrier power level is achieved. The modulating signal is amplified by a Class A audio amplifier and is then applied to a Class B push-pull amplifier. The output of the Class B stage is coupled into the anode circuit of the final stage and amplitude-modulates the high-level carrier wave. High-level modulation offers an advantage in that high-efficiency Class C amplifier stages can be used throughout the high-frequency part of the transmitter. The overall efficiency of the transmitter is then high. The disadvantage associated with high-level modulation is in the high audio-frequency power which the Class B stage must supply to adequately modulate the output stage, which demands an expensive and physically large circuit.

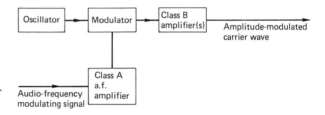

Fig. 6.8 Low-level amplitude-modulation transmitter

Fig. 6.8 shows the block schematic diagram of a LOW-LEVEL AMPLITUDE-MODULATION TRANSMITTER. The modulation process is now carried out at a low level and the modulated wave is then amplified to the required power level. The demands on the audio-frequency section of the transmitter are now much easier and cheaper to satisfy. Since the carrier wave is amplitude-modulated at a low level it cannot be raised to the desired transmitter output power level by high-efficiency Class C stages; instead Class B stages must be adopted, with a consequent reduction in the overall efficiency of the transmitter.

Many high-frequency communication transmitters carry single-sideband (s.s.b.) and/or independent sideband (i.s.b.) telephony signals. These signals are produced in a separate *drive unit* whose low-level output is applied to the input of the main transmitter for amplification to the required power level and translation to the appropriate part of the frequency spectrum.

High-frequency communications transmitters must rapidly change frequency as propagation conditions vary. To reduce the time taken to change the operating frequency, modern transmitters generally employ wideband circuits throughout most stages, and automatically tune and load the output stage.

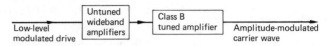

Fig. 6.9 Self-tuning transmitter

The basic block diagram of a *self-tuning* h.f. communication transmitter is shown in Fig. 6.9. The frequency of the input signal provided by the drive unit is sensed by control circuitry (not shown) and this circuitry automatically tunes the Class B output stage to the input frequency.

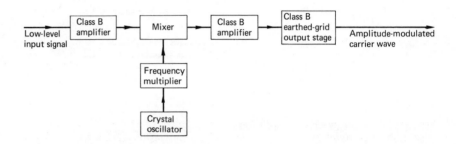

Fig. 6.10 High-frequency communication transmitter

Another type of h.f. communication transmitter which can transmit independent sideband telephony signals is shown in block diagram form in Fig. 6.10. The input drive signal is at the constant frequency of 3.1 MHz and is amplified before it is applied to the input of a mixer circuit. The crystal oscillator operates at a frequency such that, after multiplication, it will combine in the mixer with the drive signal to produce a difference frequency that is at the desired operating frequency. The difference frequency is selected and amplified by the Class B output stage. Here the power level of the signal is increased to the wanted value. Tuning of all the variable-frequency stages is automatic.

Frequency Stability

The frequency at which a radio transmitter operates must be maintained constant to within internationally agreed limits to avoid interference with adjacent (in frequency) channels. In the case of s.s.b. and i.s.b. systems the suppressed carrier must be re-inserted at the receiver with the correct frequency. This requirement will clearly be made harder if the carrier frequency at the transmitter is not constant. The oscillator from which the transmitter carrier frequency is derived must be of stable frequency, both short- and long-term. If the operating frequency of a transmitter is frequently changed, a variable-frequency oscillator of some kind must be fitted but it will then be difficult to achieve the desired frequency stability.

The highest frequency stability is obtained with a *crystal oscillator*. At frequencies near the higher end of the h.f. band it is customary to employ a crystal oscillator operating at a low frequency and then to use one or more stages of frequency multiplication to obtain the wanted transmitted frequency. A crystal oscillator is a fixed-frequency circuit, and if a transmitter is to operate at different frequencies it will be necessary to switch into circuit different crystals. Many modern transmitters use a technique known as *frequency synthesis* [see RSIII] to derive all the necessary frequencies. Typically, the frequency stability of a high-frequency transmitter is ± 1 part in 10^6, i.e. ± 1 Hz if the carrier frequency is 10 MHz.

Continuous Wave Transmitters

A sinusoidal carrier wave can be used to transmit telegraphy signals if it is switched on and off in accordance with the chosen telegraph code [see TSII]. Usually the Morse code is chosen. The carrier wave is said to be continuous because, when it is switched on, none of its parameters, i.e. its amplitude, frequency or phase, are varied. The carrier frequency can be switched on and off at a number of different points in a radio transmitter but it is most usual to key the output stage. This practice means that the keying is carried out at a point remote from the oscillator and ensures that the keying process does not alter the carrier frequency. The KEYING can be achieved in several different ways but the two common methods are illustrated by Fig. 6.11. Fig. 6.11a shows anode circuit keying; when the key is operated, the h.t. supply voltage is applied to the anode of the valve and the carrier wave appears at the output terminals of the circuit. Since high voltages are involved in the anode circuit, the key would normally be operated via a relay and not directly in order to ensure the safety of the operator. An alternative method of switching the carrier on and off is shown by Fig. 6.11b and consists of biasing the valve so far beyond cut-off that it does not conduct even at the peaks of the positive half-cycles of the input voltage. When the key is open, the valve has its normal Class B or Class C bias voltage applied via inductor L_1. When the key is operated, an extra bias voltage is applied of sufficient magnitude to ensure that the valve does not conduct. Transistor versions of these circuits are available for use in low-power transmitters.

The block schematic diagram of a c.w. telegraphy transmitter is shown in Fig. 6.12. A crystal oscillator is used to ensure that the carrier frequency radiated by the transmitter is extremely stable. The oscillator frequency is multiplied to the desired transmission frequency and is then amplified, by one or more Class C tuned amplifiers, to the level required to fully drive the output stage. The output stage raises the carrier power to the desired level and is keyed on and off using one of the methods previously outlined.

The process of suddenly interrupting a sinusoidal carrier wave generates a large number of harmonics and these are liable to cause interference with neighbouring carrier frequencies. To reduce the bandwidth occupied by a c.w. signal it is customary to fit a suitable filter circuit to the keying arrangement.

Output Stages

The output stage of a radio transmitter has a number of functions to perform. It must develop the radio-frequency power output that the transmitter is to produce and must do so with the maximum possible efficiency. The selectivity of the stage must be such that the side frequencies of the signal are transmitted but unwanted harmonics are not. Further the output stage should be operated linearly and should not be prone to unwanted oscillations, known as *parasitic oscillations*. Lastly, the stage should be easy to tune to the operating frequency and to couple with the optimum efficiency to the aerial feeder; in many modern equipments the tuning and loading of the final stage is carried out automatically.

Tetrode valves are used in the final stage of many h.f. transmitters mainly because they have a higher gain than triodes, and the screening effect of the screen grid simplifies neutralization problems. Tetrodes possess the disadvantage of dissipating power at the screen grid and so the higher-power transmitters often use a triode output stage. Triodes suffer from unwanted feedback via their anode-grid capacitance and need to be neutralized. To avoid the complexity of a neutralization circuit, triode output stages often employ the earthed-grid connection. The output stage must be coupled efficiently to the aerial feeder which is normally of the unbalanced coaxial type within the radio station building. Some of the ways in which the output stage of a low-level transmitter can be coupled to the aerial feeder are shown in Fig. 6.13.

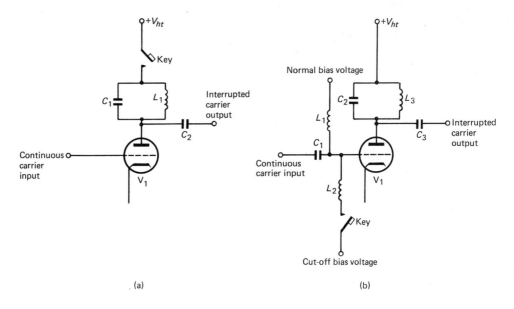

Fig. 6.11 Keying methods

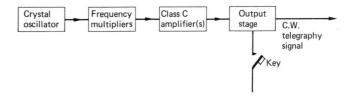

Fig. 6.12 C.W. telegraphy transmitter

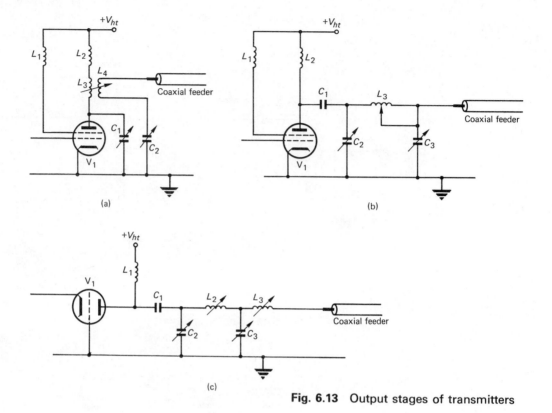

Fig. 6.13 Output stages of transmitters

In Fig. 6.13a a tetrode valve is coupled to the coaxial feeder by means of the mutual inductance between inductors L_3 and L_4. The load into which the valve works can be adjusted to the optimum value by appropriate adjustment of the coupling between L_3 and L_4. Inductors L_1 and L_2 are provided as radio-frequency chokes to stop r.f. currents entering the h.t. power supply line. The anode circuit is tuned to resonate at the desired operating frequency by adjustment of capacitor C_1, while resonating the secondary circuit L_4C_2 ensures that maximum current flows into the feeder. An alternative output stage-feeder coupling arrangement which reduces the number of variable components by one is illustrated by Fig. 6.13b. In this circuit the anode of the tetrode valve is coupled by capacitor C_1 to a π-type output network. The stage is tuned by the variable capacitors C_2 and C_3 while optimum coupling to the feeder is achieved by suitable adjustment of the value of inductor L_3. L_1 and L_2 are radio-frequency chokes. Fig. 6.13c shows the usual way in which a triode output stage is coupled to its feeder. It can be seen to be similar to the tetrode circuit of Fig. 6.13b, except that two inductors must be adjusted for optimum valve-feeder coupling.

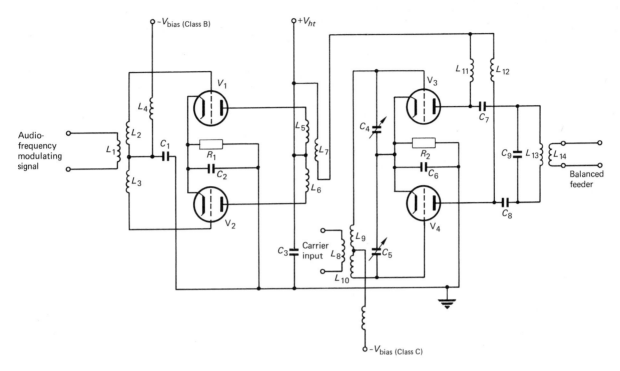

Fig. 6.14 Output stage of a high-level transmitter

Fig. 6.14 shows the circuit diagram of the output stage of a high-level modulation transmitter. The Class C output stage has two triode valves V_3 and V_4 connected in push-pull for increased power output. The output voltage of the Class B modulating stage is developed across inductor L_7 and modulates the h.t. voltage supplied to V_3 and V_4. The functions of the various components are left as an exercise for the reader (Exercise 6.4). In practice, a circuit of this type would be fitted with capacitors connected between the anode of one valve and the grid of the other for neutralization purposes, and with resistors in series with the triode grids to prevent unwanted oscillations.

Matching Aerial Feeder to Transmitter

For a transmitter output stage to deliver the maximum possible power to the feeder connecting it to the aerial, two requirements must be satisfied. Firstly, the anode circuit must be resonant at the frequency of operation and, secondly, the input impedance of the feeder must be transformed by the coupling network into the optimum load for the output valve. The anode circuit is tuned by the correct adjustment of its inductance and/or capacitance, and the optimum load is obtained by varying the inductive coupling between the anode circuit and the feeder. The optimum load for the output valve is that value which provides the maximum output power possible without exceeding the voltage, current or power ratings of the output valve. To achieve the maximum output power it is also necessary for the voltage driving the output stage to be large enough and this may require careful adjustment of the coupling between the driver stage and the output stage.

The procedure adopted to tune and load an output stage varies in detail with the particular transmitter used but the general principles are as follows. The coupling between the feeder and the output stage is reduced to a small value. The anode circuit of the output stage is then tuned to resonance at the operating frequency, resonance being indicated by the anode current attaining a minimum value. (The reason why resonance is indicated by minimum anode current should be known. When the anode tuned circuit is resonant its impedance is at its maximum value and is purely resistive, and the anode voltage will vary in antiphase with the grid voltage. When the grid voltage is at the peak of its positive half cycle, the anode current has its maximum value and the anode voltage has its minimum value. If the anode circuit is not resonant, the anode voltage is not at its minimum value when the positive peak of the grid voltage occurs and so the peak anode current is larger.) The coupling between the output stage and the feeder is now gradually increased, anode circuit resonance being maintained, until maximum power is delivered to the feeder.

When a π-type coupling network (Fig. 6.13) is used a slightly different procedure is followed. With a reduced value of h.t. supply voltage, capacitor C_3 is short-circuited and C_2 adjusted to give resonance. The short circuit is then removed and C_3 adjusted to transfer maximum output voltage to the feeder. The h.t. supply voltage is then increased to its correct value and C_2 re-adjusted, if necessary, to restore the resonant condition.

Exercises

6.1. With the aid of a circuit diagram explain the action of a crystal-controlled oscillator for a h.f. transmitter. State briefly the precautions necessary to obtain good frequency stability. What order of frequency stability would you expect to find in such transmitters? Why is such stability necessary?

6.2. Draw the circuit diagram and explain the operation of the final r.f. stage of a high-power radio transmitter. Show how modulation of the signal is achieved.

6.3. Draw the block diagram of a c.w. telegraphy transmitter. Explain the function of each block.

6.4. List the function of each component shown in the circuit of Fig. 6.14. Explain, with waveform sketches, the operation of the circuit.

6.5. Redraw each of the output stages given in Fig. 6.13 and add suitable input circuits. Explain the purpose of each new component drawn.

6.6. Draw the block schematic diagram of an amplitude-modulation transmitter. State whether your circuit is of the high-level or the low-level type and explain its operation.

6.7. Describe, in your own words, a procedure for matching the output stage of a radio transmitter to its aerial feeder.

6.8. Draw the circuit diagram of a Class C r.f. power amplifier using a tetrode valve and explain its operation. Illustrate your answer with appropriate waveform sketches.

6.9. Draw the circuit diagram of an anode-modulated Class C amplifier and explain its operation.

Short Exercises

6.10. Draw and explain the circuit of the final amplifier stage in an amplitude-modulation radio transmitter.

6.11. State briefly why an amplitude-modulation radio transmitter (*a*) should have good frequency stability, (*b*) may include a frequency multiplier.

6.12. Explain, with the aid of waveform sketches, what is meant by Class B and Class C bias of a triode valve.

6.13. Compare the use of tetrode valves in Class B and Class C r.f. power amplifiers.

6.14. What is meant by frequency multiplication. Outline a way in which it can be performed.

6.15. Explain the function of each component shown in the push-pull Class C power amplifier of Fig. 6.5.

7 Communication Systems

Introduction

Public telephone systems are designed to make it possible for a connection to be established between any two points within the network. In the case of a short-distance connection the transmission performance will depend mainly upon the quality of the telephone instruments. Longer-distance connections will be routed wholly or partly over multi-channel telephony systems, mainly for economic reasons. In turn, the multi-channel systems may be routed over wideband coaxial cable or, alternatively, over a channel in a u.h.f. or an s.h.f. radio relay system. Both systems are also capable of transmitting television signals. The principles of operation of multi-channel telephony systems and the construction of coaxial cable have been described elsewhere [TSII] while radio-relay systems will be described later in this chapter.

International Circuits

International circuits are routed overseas mainly by means of multi-channel systems which are transmitted via either a submarine coaxial cable or an earth satellite. SUBMARINE CABLES have been installed throughout the world for many years and, for example, such routes exist between the United Kingdom and several points on the European mainland, between the United Kingdom and the U.S.A., and between the United Kingdom and Canada. Most submarine cable systems are operated with transmission in one direction occupying one band of frequencies and transmission in the other direction in a higher frequency band. Modern submarine systems transmit frequencies up to 13.7 MHz, providing 1840 channels each of 3 kHz bandwidth. They are designed for the utmost reliability because of the obvious difficulties with any necessary repairs.

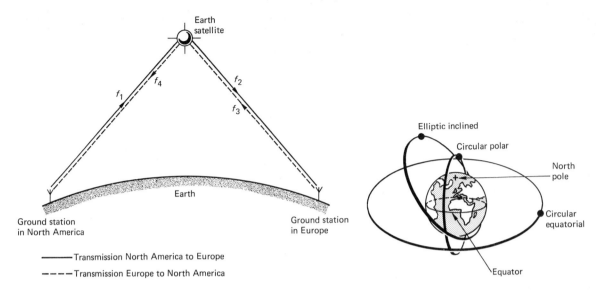

Fig. 7.1 An earth satellite communication system

Fig. 7.2 Some possible earth satellite orbits (From the *Post Office Electrical Engineers Journal*)

Submarine cables are extremely expensive and their traffic-carrying capacity is not sufficient to satisfy the demand for international telecommunications. In order to increase considerably the available traffic capacity of international telecommunication networks, an earth satellite system has now been provided.

The basic principle of an EARTH SATELLITE communication system is shown in Fig. 7.1. The ground stations are fully integrated with their national telephone networks and, in addition, the European stations are fully interconnected with each other. Four frequencies are used: the North American station transmits on frequency f_1 and receives frequency f_4, the European stations transmit frequency f_3 and receive frequency f_2. The function of the satellite is to receive the signals transmitted to it, frequency change them (f_1 to f_2 or f_3 to f_4), and then amplify them before transmission to the ground station at the other end of the link.

An earth satellite can be placed into a number of different orbits around the Earth; possible orbits include circular and elliptical orbits in the equatorial and polar planes of the Earth, or inclined at some angle to one of these planes. Three possible orbits are shown in Fig. 7.2.

Communication satellites, known as Intelsat III and IV, are operated as a global system by COMSAT (Communication Satellite Corporation) on behalf of an international body known as INTELSAT (International Telecommunication Satellite Consortium). The system employs communication satellites travelling in the circular equatorial orbit at a height of 35880 km. This particular orbit is known as the synchronous orbit because a satellite travelling in it appears to be stationary above a particular part of the Earth's surface. In the INTELSAT system the satellites are stationary above the Atlantic, Indian, and Pacific oceans. A large number of earth stations, each operated by the telephone administration of the country concerned, have access to a satellite. In the United Kingdom the earth station at Goonhilly is operated by the Post Office. Each of the earth stations transmits its traffic to a satellite on the particular carrier frequencies allocated to it in the band 5.925—6.425 GHz. All the signals received by a satellite are transmitted back to Earth on carrier frequencies in the band 3.700—4.200 GHz, and each earth station selects the particular carrier frequencies that carry traffic destined to that station.

Augmenting the international telecommunication network of submarine cable and earth satellite multi-channel systems are a number of FOUR-WIRE RADIO LINKS operating in the high-frequency band 3–30 MHz. Fig. 7.3 shows a typical arrangement. A form of s.s.b. working, known as independent sideband (i.s.b.), enables either two high-quality or four commercial-quality (0–3 kHz) speech circuits to be accommodated in a 12 kHz bandwidth. A subscriber in one country is connected, via the junction and trunk network of that country, to his international telephone exchange. Here an operator takes details of the call and makes contact, via a radio circuit to the required country, with an operator in the distant international exchange. The connection is then completed by the foreign operator. Increasingly nowadays, the connection can be established automatically, by dialling the correct code, without the assistance of an operator. Signals passing between the two subscribers are at audio frequency up to the radio link itself; at the transmitter the signals amplitude modulate a carrier in the h.f. band and the resulting waveform is radiated to the distant receiver. Different frequencies are employed for the two directions of transmission over the radio link to eliminate the possibility of singing around the loop.

Ship Radio-Telephones

Telephonic communication is often required between a telephone subscriber and a ship at sea, and the arrangement for setting up such a connection is shown in Fig. 7.4. The telephone subscriber is connected, via the trunk network, with the control centre. The control centre is linked by cable to a

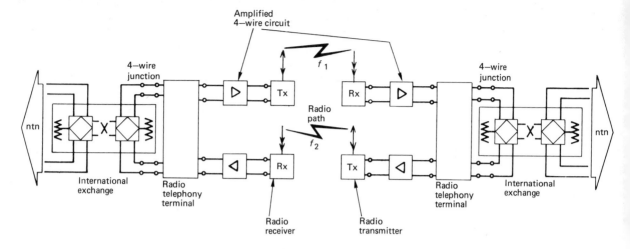

Fig. 7.3 An international radio-telephony circuit

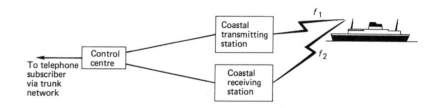

Fig. 7.4 Shore-to-ship telephone connection

number of coastal transmitting and receiving radio stations, each of which transmits or receives to or from a different part of the world. The control centre establishes the required connection with a distant ship via the appropriate pair of radio stations. To provide good coverage of a particular area of the world, each transmitting station transmits on several different frequencies at the same time.

A similar arrangement is adopted for telegraphic communication with ships at sea, the main differences being that teleprinters are used and are connected to the control centre via the Telex network.

The CCITT and the CCIR

To ensure compatibility between the telephone networks of different countries that play a part in a particular international telephone connection, it is necessary that carrier frequencies, bandwidths, noise levels and other parameters involved are standardized. The task of specifying the parameters of telecommunication systems destined for possible use in the international network has been given to the *International Telecommunication Union* (ITU). The ITU carries out its standardization work through two committees; the *International Consultative Committee for Radio* (CCIR) and the *Consultative Committee for Telephony and Telegraphy* (CCITT). The two committees meet at intervals to consider international telecommunication problems and policy, and include representatives from most, if not all, countries of the world. Sub-committees are set up to study particular telecommunication problems and to produce recommendations for the solution of those problems. The recommendations of the CCITT and CCIR are not mandatory but most equipments are manufactured to conform with those which are relevant. The application of CCITT/CCIR recommendations to equipment which will be used for purely national routes is a matter for the particular administration concerned, and for example, not all Post Office equipment conforms to recommended values. On the other hand, it is important that all equipment likely to be taken into use when an international connection is established should conform to all the relevant recommendations, otherwise many connections could have an inadequate transmission performance.

Among the CCITT/CCIR recommendations in current use are those covering the following topics:

(1) The carrier frequencies and the channel bandwidths to be used by the basic 12-channel telephony group.
(2) The way in which 12-channel groups can be combined together to form larger capacity coaxial systems.
(3) An international trunk switching plan.
(4) The frequency stabilities required for radio transmitters operating in different frequency bands.
(5) The allocation of frequencies to different services.

UHF and SHF Radio Relay Systems

Radio relay systems operating in a number of fixed bands in the u.h.f. and s.h.f. bands form an integral part of the trunk network in the United Kingdom. One system is able to carry several wideband channels each of which, in turn, can carry many hundreds of commercial-quality speech channels and/or a television signal. The composite signal carried by a channel is known as the *baseband*.

The basic block schematic diagram of a radio relay system is shown in Fig. 7.5. The mode of propagation at these frequencies is the space wave. High-gain, very directive aerials are used with a transmitted power level in the region of 1 watt and

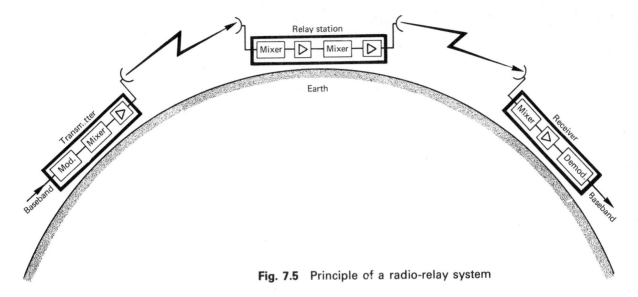

Fig. 7.5 Principle of a radio-relay system

this permits links of nearly "line of sight" length to be provided. When, as is generally the case, longer distances are to be covered, a number of relay stations must be appropriately spaced along the length of the route. In Fig. 7.5 only one radio relay station has been shown to simplify the drawing. At the transmitter the baseband signal modulates a 70 MHz carrier (this being a CCIR recommended frequency) and the frequency-modulated output is applied to a mixer. At this stage the signal is shifted to the appropriate part of the u.h.f. or the s.h.f. band and is then amplified before it is fed to the transmitting aerial. At the relay station, the received signal is translated to the intermediate frequency of 70 MHz, amplified, and then shifted to a new part of the frequency spectrum before further amplification and radiation towards the receiver. At the receiver, the incoming signal is converted to the 70 MHz intermediate frequency, amplified, and is then demodulated to produce the original baseband signal. The baseband signal may then be transmitted to some further location by means of a coaxial pair or, if the audio channels are wanted at this location, the signal is applied to the receive-end terminal equipment of a multi-channel telephony system.

Exercises

7.1. Explain why there is a need for CCITT and CCIR recommendations regarding the performance specification of line and radio communication systems. List some examples.

7.2. A telephone connection is to be established between a point in the United Kingdom and a town in the U.S.A. Draw block diagrams showing two possible ways in which the connection could be set up.

7.3. Draw the block schematic diagram of an international high-frequency radio-telephony link. Describe the function of each block shown in your diagram and state the disadvantages inherent in this system.

7.4. Discuss the reasons why submarine cables, earth satellites and h.f. radio links are all employed in the international telephone network.

7.5. Draw block diagrams of the following simple communication systems:

(*a*) An overseas radio-telephone link between customers in different continents,

(*b*) An overseas telephone call between a customer in the United Kingdom and a ship at sea.

State in both cases the carrier frequencies and channel bandwidths.

Short Exercises

7.6. Discuss the place of land and submarine coaxial telephony systems in communication networks.

7.7. Discuss the place of radio relay and earth satellite systems in communication networks.

7.8. What is meant by each of the following sets of initials: (*a*) COMSAT, (*b*) CCITT, (*c*) CCIR, (*d*) ITU, (*e*) INTELSAT.

Numerical Answers to Exercises

1.1 $Z_0 = 300\,\Omega$, 2.5×10^8 m/s, 16.67 mA

1.4   500 W

1.8 $50\,\Omega$, $50\,\Omega$

1.9 $340\,\Omega$, 2.65×10^8 m/s

1.10   59.5 pF/m, 214.3 nH/m

1.17   12°, 24°

2.1   0.268 m, 0.282 m, 0.255 m, 0.08 m

2.5   0.186 m, 0.196 m, 0.177 m, 0.056 m

2.6   2.6 dB

2.12   1.67 m, 1.75 m, 1.58 m, 0.5 m

2.14   180 W, 41.86%

2.15   80%, 50.48 kW

2.16   3.98 dB

2.18   13 dB

2.26   37.5 m

4.20   11.18:1

5.2   450 kHz, 12 kHz, 2300 kHz

Radio Systems II:
Learning Objectives (TEC)

(A) Radiation. Aerials and Lines

(B) Radio Receivers

(C) Radio Transmitters

Index